125 Years of Caring in Dublin

In memory of Lar

(1961–1997)

125 Years of Caring in Dublin

Our Lady's Hospice
Harold's Cross
1879–2004

T. M. Healy

A. & A. Farmar

British Library cataloguing in Publication Data
A CIP catalogue record for this book is available from the
British Library

Edited, designed and set by A. & A. Farmar
Printed and bound by ColourBooks

ISBN (HB) 1-899047-18-2

First published in 2004
by
A. & A. Farmar
Beech House
78 Ranelagh Village
Dublin 6
Ireland
Tel: +353 1 496 3625
Fax: + 353 1 497 0107
Email: afarmar@iol.ie
Web: farmarbooks.com

Contents

Foreword

Dr Tim Healy notes in this comprehensive work that the Hospice, situated in Our Lady's Mount, Harold's Cross, has always been an intimate part of the history of Dublin. For many Dubliners it also conjures up memories of infant, junior and secondary schooldays, social and pastoral services, Our Lady's Sodality and a myriad of other ministries that the Sisters of Charity developed to respond to the educational and pastoral needs of the people in the area. That history has yet to be written. In the pages of this book, Dr Healy tells the story of the Hospice itself and does so in a manner that is historically rich and very readable. He has also admirably situated his historical analysis within the human story of love and caring service that is synonymous with Our Lady's Hospice.

Mary Aikenhead, the foundress of the Sisters of Charity, was a pioneer in many ways. She is best known perhaps for her establishment of St Vincent's Hospital in Dublin, the first hospital to be staffed and run by women in Ireland. While the Hospice began after her death, she spent the last thirteen years of her life in the Convent in Harold's Cross, the building which now houses the Heritage Centre. Though she would not recognise much of the present campus, she would be very much 'at home' with what Our Lady's Mount has now become and particularly so in the excellent services offered to so many sick and vulnerable people and their families in the Hospice itself. This book is a tribute to all of those people who, over the years since its foundation, have helped make the Hospice a centre of excellence which is widely known and internationally respected.

The Hospice has developed into what it is today because of the commitment, enthusiasm, vision and support of the many people who have worked there down through the years, both in voluntary and professional capacities. In the following pages, Dr Healy outlines and analyses the many factors which have contributed to the growth and development of the Hospice, but above all he has captured the 'heart' of all it has been and is to the people who find there a service that respects their dignity, reassures their fears and combines the best in medical expertise with a compassion and understanding of pastoral care.

Sister Una O'Neill, Superior General
Religious Sisters of Charity, Ireland

Acknowledgements

Encouraged by Sister Francis Rose O'Flynn, I offered to write a short account of Our Lady's Hospice. Steeped in the history of the Hospice as she is, she pointed me to the original sources and has also given the view for the future of the Hospice.

Sister Ignatius Phelan, one of the founders of Palliative and Home Care, readily supplied her account of these beginnings; Sister Marie Bernadette, the archivist of the Congregation, gave me free access and much direction to the relevant papers. Others of the present Sisters are mentioned in the text and the Congregation's Superior General, Sister Una O'Neill, has kindly provided a foreword, though it is not free from exaggeration. Sister Helen Cunningham's holograph about the Chapel was an essential source for details.

Current and former medical staff were generous with information and are quoted in the appropriate places. Michael Murphy found annual returns to the Hospitals Trust which gave facts unavailable elsewhere. Patricia Pierce cheerfully transcribed my many pencil drafts to printed form. She also found and chose many of the illustrations. Other members of staff contributed and are mentioned in the text.

Tony and Anna Farmar, as always, proved helpful publishers and decisive editors.

On the home front, Vi provided succour and salty humour. Son Tim made the bar charts having persuaded me graphs were outdated. Jim furnished dates for the tenure of office of various Ministers of Health. Maev O'Higgins continues to arrange her kind of support.

To all of these people and to countless unnamed I am deeply grateful.

Introduction

Our Lady's Hospice Harold's Cross has changed greatly since its foundation in 1879. The two most striking new influences have come from external factors in the decade after the Second World War: these were the arrival of antibiotics and of state medical care.

The ethos of the Sisters of Charity is characterised by their motto which may be translated as 'The love of God drives us onwards— *Caritas Christi urget nos*'. As in most countries the number of Sisters has dwindled as vocations fall. At present there is in the Hospice a working community of but a few Sisters. No community numbers are given in any of the Annual Reports and Annals of the Hospice. Medical doctors are mentioned but seldom, and total numbers of nursing or other staff are not mentioned at all for 70 years. Patient numbers, diagnoses, discharges and deaths are available, thus providing essential data. Despite these lacunae what is certain is that the staff to patient ratio has increased manyfold—again a change experienced in other hospitals as part of the growing complexity of medical and ancillary care. Continuing education—something hardly heard of in the world of hospitals and hospices a few decades ago—has expanded exponentially.

To survive in a healthy state any institution must change. For me the extent and success of these changes in the Hospice during the 125 years of its existence have been the most interesting result of my digging and delving into the past. Making all of this clear is the aim of this brief history.

The character and personality of the workers in any hospital is important. Whose was the charisma that spurred others to action?

There are insightful glimpses of the personality of the early Sisters available in the Annals and obituary notices of the Order. Oral tradition about the relative importance of various people in the past has survived. The written and oral accounts referred to are listed under 'References' at the end of this book. There too will be found a chronology and also lists of the leading figures who have worked in Our Lady's Hospice since 1879. There is also a list of all staff working in Our Lady's Hospice in 2004.

Where no references are given the facts and quotes are from the Annals of the Hospice. It is the practice of the Religious Sisters of Charity to send, every five years, summaries of the activities of each House to the Generalate of the Congregation. The Annals are kept in the Archival Department in Sandymount, Dublin. Depending on the anonymous author of the time these invaluable accounts vary in length and content, but they are the only primary historical source for most of the 125 years of Our Lady's Hospice. Any comments or opinions given are my own and not to be attributed to the Religious Sisters of Charity or to any others.

One point needs emphasis. This is not an account of all the happenings in Our Lady's Mount—the early name for the site where the Hospice still stands. The novice house for aspirants to the Order preceded the Hospice. Primary and secondary schools, sodalities, visitations to the homes of the poor and many other activities were based in Harold's Cross. By the end of the second millennium the three core Hospice activities of Extended Care, Palliative Care and Rheumatology and Rehabilitation had been established. The change from a 'Hospice for the Dying' (the title until 1964) to 'Our Lady's Hospice' with these three functions is the subject of this book.

1 Hospices through the ages

That we build on the past is a truth sometimes forgotten. New ideas are not born in a vacuum. A brief account of early hospices and later palliative care units will put the genesis and growth of Our Lady's Hospice into the context of its times.

The meaning of the word hospice has changed over the centuries. The first recorded one was in the fourth century AD when it meant a place of rest and recovery for pilgrims. But it would be very surprising if such places of refuge for sick and weary travellers had not existed for eons. Its use in English dates from about 1818 when its meaning was similar—the hospices in the Alps run by the monks of St Bernard are given as an example.[1] Later in the nineteenth century the first hospice specifically for the dying was founded in France.

Jeanne Garnier was a widow living in Paris. Married at the age of 21 years, in rapid succession she lost her husband and her three children. Inspired by their deaths she then enlisted the help of other widows to found 'L'Association des Dames du Calvaire'. Within a year their hospice opened in 1843 in Garnier's native city of Lyons. At first the hospice was for women with advanced cancer. The ethos was characterised by 'a respectful familiarity and an attitude of prayer and calm in the face of death'. By the end of the century there were other 'Calvaire' hospices in Paris, New York and elsewhere. An American author[2] has written of their influence extending to present times on the founding of palliative care units in the USA.

A century before Garnier's hospices there was founded in Dublin the Royal Hospital for Incurables in Donnybrook. In some ways it resembled the much later Harold's Cross foundation. But it was not just a hospice for the dying as Helen Burke has pointed out:

'There were two reasons for establishing the Hospital: to offer care and shelter to people who were incurably ill and to remove "those miserable objects who were offensive to sight from the streets"'.[3]

'The Incurables in Donnybrook' is still active today under the more accurate name of 'The Royal Hospital'. A hundred years after it started another hospital for 'incurables' opened its doors in Cork. No Royal title here, it was called St Patrick's. Later the name of part of the site was changed to Marymount, just as Greenmount in Harold's Cross had become Our Lady's Mount. The reason for the likeness in names is simple: both places were founded by the Sisters of Charity. For Cork this was possible because of a bequest from a medical man, Patrick Murphy, a name which may explain the title of the hospital. Murphy's father and sister had died during the Famine. In 1849 he made a will leaving his property to the Sisters with the request that they build and run a hospital for incurable cases of cancer. Nearly twenty years after making this will he died and by 1870 the first patients were admitted to the new hospital. Murphy had stipulated that the building must be finished within two years of his death—this condition was honoured, rare though this may be.

A decade after the Cork hospital was built the Hospice opened in Harold's Cross. Both places now have palliative care units; both originally were filled mainly by patients with tuberculosis, despite Dr Murphy's hopes that his would be a cancer hospital. Both always admitted dying and terminal patients and both still do.

The Hospice in Harold's Cross has always claimed to be the first hospice established in these islands, as well as being responsible for founding the first hospice in London—St Joseph's in Hackney. These are valid claims of which the Sisters may well be proud. Can St Patrick's in Cork claim priority because of its earlier foundation? Is it a question of semantics—hospice or hospital? These are questions of no importance when quality work continues to be the goal whether in Dublin, Cork or London (see Note 1: Australia).

Appendix 1 includes a chronological list of hospice and palliative care foundations. Priority, the origin of good ideas and the influence of particular leaders, such as Mary Aikenhead, Anna Gaynor and Cicely Saunders, all pale in importance compared to the resulting benefit to humanity. Good ideas take time to come to fruition: as happened for Harold's Cross and in many fields of social welfare reaction to an urgent need will depend on what is possible at that time and place.

Palliative care became a new speciality in the mid-twentieth century. This will be discussed later when Our Lady's Hospice developed this modern way of helping the dying. These and other changes in the Hospice have all one cause: whatever the reason people live longer.

The year the Hospice started is notable for an event of national importance in this country: the foundation of the Land League in Strokestown, Co. Mayo by Michael Davitt. Later that same year of 1879 two delegates of the League were sent to the USA to raise funds: Charles Stewart Parnell and John Dillon. Not only the Sisters in Harold's Cross were stirring in those days.

2 Nineteenth-century Dublin

Dublin in the last quarter of the nineteenth century was a city with a rising population. By the 1900s it was over one quarter of a million people. By the 1920s the numbers in city and suburbs totalled over 400,000. This increase in the size of cities was experienced world wide. Where Dublin was out of step was in the incidence of fatal infections: the level for all kinds of tuberculosis was twice that of London or Glasgow. For measles the number of fatal cases was triple that of London as was that for typhoid—these are the 1899 figures. The belief that such fevers were infectious and spread by bacteria grew but slowly during this time. Ireland lagged behind in public health measures, and more particularly in their implementation.

In the year Our Lady's Hospice opened its doors to the dying the annual death rate in Dublin was at its highest compared to other Continental and North American cities: it was an 'annual waste of some 3,500 lives' as Joseph O'Brien puts it.[5] In Dublin the mortality rate of 33.6 per 1,000 of the population in 1899 (16 per cent of all deaths) was the highest for twenty years, topped only by Calcutta.

That housing was very poor and overcrowding rampant relate closely to the incidence of contagious disease. One quarter of Dublin's population lived in single rooms, more than half of which lodged three or more people.[6] These were the tenement houses which had been visited daily by the Sisters of Charity for more than 30 years before the Hospice was founded: the cramped and often squalid conditions where birth, life and death all mingled, were a major reason for starting Our Lady's Hospice. Home visiting continued

The original house, seen from the avenue

after the 1879 foundation. A century later such domiciliary visits, if for very different reasons, were to become a keystone of palliative care. Housing had improved and lay workers had replaced the Sisters to a large extent but the underlying principle remained the same: personal contact with the sick in their own environment by staff animated by the same ideals.

The public water supply, sewage disposal, food quality, washing facilities—these and the factors above are all part of public health. In Dublin when the Hospice started the Public Health Committee of the Corporation was in existence for only a few years. The sewage of the city ran untreated directly into the river: 'the summer effluvia of the Liffey made themselves offensively patent to visitors'.[7] By the century's end there was some improvement in sanitation but not in the death rate. One major advance was that in Dublin's water supply: the Vartry Water Works began its operations in 1868. Before this the citizens relied on a supply from the canals. Earlier still it was from the Poddle River, known to the residents of the Hospice and of Harold's Cross as a cause of flooding, but not as a supply of dubious water. For the Hospice Vartry water meant much: safe drinking water and safe waste disposal; water closets (WCs) came into use in Dublin at this time.

The last and most important point to be made about Dublin in the late nineteenth century is the level of poverty. Accurate measurement of this is not easy. Unemployment figures and social welfare were far in the future. Nearly 7,000 paupers got indoor relief every day in the two workhouses, where another 1,000 gathered twice a week to get a 'hand out' of bread, tea, sugar, and occasionally meat. Friaries, such as Merchant's Quay and Dominic Street dispensed similar necessities of life—tea consumption has always been high on the list of priorities in the Irish diet.

'The stench of poverty' is a hackneyed phrase but it is something that lingers long. A French woman visited Ireland and Dublin not long after the Hospice was founded. She has left a description of Patrick Street—a mile below the Hospice:

> Rows of tumble-down mouldy-looking houses reeking of dirt and oozing with the disgusting smell of the accumulated filth of many generations. . . . Shops expose for sale rancid bacon . . . musty turnips and bad potatoes . . . the smell is mixed with that of bad cabbage, tobacco and paraffin oil, coming out in puffs from the half doors of the hovels.[8]

A clean bed and a faint smell of soap and carbolic made a change for Dubliners who died in the Hospice.

3 Foundation and early days

Our Lady's Hospice in Harold's Cross, Dublin was founded and is still run by the Religious Sisters of Charity (RSC). For many years these were called the Irish Sisters of Charity to distinguish them from the older French order, now the Daughters of Charity. For this account they will be called 'the Sisters'.

The order began in 1815 and was the brainchild of a Cork lady and convert to Roman Catholicism, Mary Aikenhead. Before her death in 1858 she had founded thirteen houses around Ireland—their work ranging from missions to the poor, schools, orphanages and a hospital in Dublin. The hospital was St Vincent's on St Stephen's Green and was founded in 1834. Here lived Aikenhead, here she stayed and ruled her Congregation for the next eleven years. By the end of the nineteenth century the number of foundations in Dublin alone had reached seventeen. The most recent biography of Aikenhead and her work is by Blake[9] and the best early account is by Sara Atkinson,[10] a lady who knew Aikenhead and who, like her, was a convert to Roman Catholicism. Formidable as were Mary Aikenhead's achievements, lasting as is her influence, they are outside the scope of this book. What is relevant is the purchase by her in 1845 of the site where Our Lady's Hospice in Harold's Cross came to be built. Greenmount was a late eighteenth-century house on raised ground south-west and above the Grand Canal. The owners were people called Webb, members of the Society of Friends (Quakers) (see Note 2: Lord Edward Fitzgerald). They agreed a price with the Sisters and kept their word even though a higher offer was made by the Mount Jerome Cemetery Company immediately adjacent to Greenmount.

The immediate reason for acquiring Greenmount is made clear in Atkinson's biography of Aikenhead.

> Towards the close of 1844 Mother Aikenhead suffered from frequent attacks of bronchitis. This, added to all her other maladies [which included a mistaken diagnosis of cancer of the spine] left her very weak. Dr Ferrall, always intent on prolonging this precious life, declared she must have [a] change of air. It was therefore decided to take a house in the suburbs of Dublin which would make a suitable novitiate and at the same time be the residence of the Superior General.[10]

Mary Aikenhead remained in Harold's Cross until her death in 1858.

Apart from its availability this site may have been chosen because the Harold's Cross area had a reputation for salubrity since the eighteenth century.

> The air in this neighbourhood has been considered particularly favourable to invalids. . .

> Many of the townsfolk sent delicate children there to be nursed [fostered] . . . The rural village of Harold's Cross [was well known for] its invigorating breezes blowing straight down from the mountains . . . Citizens purchased the interest of villagers and commenced the conversion of Harold's Cross into a suburb until the establishment of the Cemetery acted like a blight to the neighbourhood.[11]

Mount Jerome Cemetery was opened in the 1830s. The opening of the graveyard may have stopped the exodus of well-off Dubliners, but a century and a half later many from Dublin and beyond, rich and poor alike, are still glad to use that other facility in Harold's Cross, Our Lady's Hospice.

Fear of infection was the basis for the preference for clean country air and a raised site. It was to be many years before the causes of all these infections would be discovered, but for millennia the dangers of overcrowding, poor diet and polluted water had been known to doctors and lay folk alike. The first use found for Greenmount's big house and grounds was as a novitiate and not as a hospice. Youth was more at risk from fevers and tuberculosis and the young novices deserved a good environment as much as any future dying patient. Not for nothing was Mary Aikenhead the daughter of an apothecary, the general practitioners of the early nineteenth century (see Note 3: David Aikenhead).

It was in September 1845 that Aikenhead moved to Greenmount. Within days 20 novices and 30 Sisters followed their Superior General to what had now become the Mother House of the congregation. New buildings arose. A night school for women and girls, a Sunday school and finally in 1851 a large day school were started. As mentioned in the Introduction these activities will not be covered here.

It is ironic in view of the reputation of Harold's Cross as a healthy neighbourhood that the immediate cause of the change from novitiate to hospice should have been an outbreak of smallpox. It was not in Our Lady's Mount, however, but in Dublin city that this had started in January 1879. It led to the admission of cases to St Vincent's Hospital. Attending St Vincent's for nursing instruction was a young novice who there contracted smallpox. During the incubation period she returned as usual each night to Harold's Cross and became sick. Smallpox spreads readily and rapidly: sixteen other Sisters contracted the disease. None died.

When the epidemic was over there was insufficient room for the novices in Harold's Cross—despite the outbreak their number had grown. A move further from the city was advisable. This was to Milltown, Co. Dublin, and again to high ground, newly named Mount St Anne's. This left house-room in that other Mount, Our Lady's in Harold's Cross, and an opportunity to found a hospice for the dying . The seed for the idea of developing a place dedicated to the care of the dying had been germinating for some twelve years. Working in St Vincent's Hospital had been two Sisters named M. Charles Hynes and M. Philip Neri Russell who had seen this great need and discussed it with Aikenhead. However, other needs and

Harold's Cross in the 1830s,
showing outline of present-day Our Lady's Hospice

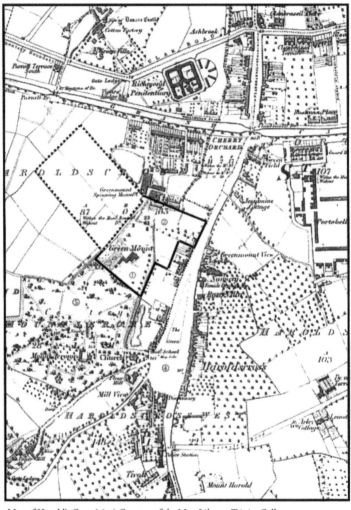

Map of Harold's Cross (1831) Courtesy of the Map Library, Trinity College

KEY

1. Our Lady's Mount   4. Park
2. Mill Pond   5. Mount Jerome Cemetery
3. Land acquired in 1910 (3 acres)

plans then demanded action, but the two nuns began their own campaign of prayer and continued it until their deaths years before the Hospice was opened. A separate account of this same incident, written a few years later, is worth quoting in full:

> Sisters in St Vincent's Hospital seeing and feeling how very hard it was to send away the poor dismissed by the doctors as beyond hope of recovery, some having very poor homes and others no friends willing to receive them, bethought themselves of having a hospice or home where these poor sufferers might be received.

Such a policy of refusal of admission was common in those days and it was the main reason for the foundation of the Hospice. Refusal of admission of the very sick may sound heartless to modern ears. Apart from a shortage of beds there were valid reasons: fear of infection of the inmates by a new patient was one; another was that in the absence of any effective treatment of many diseases such as tuberculosis and cancer the medical staff preferred to admit those they could help. In those days these were the minority.

Such admission policies, common to most hospitals at the time Our Lady's Hospice was founded, were nothing new. The first long-lasting Dublin hospital had opened its doors in 1718 and was called the Charitable Infirmary, more often known as 'Jervis Street'. When Dr Steevens' Hospital started a few years later the criteria for admission specified that, as in Jervis Street, there were 'no bars as to religion or ailments so long as the latter were not infectious'. Fever patients in Dublin were admitted to just two hospitals: the Hardwicke (1803, beside the Richmond, later St Laurence's) and Cork Street (1804). Given such admission policies a refuge for the sick poor of the city, an institution that took in the infectious, the destitute and the dying was a great need in nineteenth-century Dublin. Our Lady's Hospice filled this need.

The smallpox epidemic of 1879 has been mentioned. That winter also saw heavy snow and 'a stoppage of the sewers'. Rumour was rife about deaths among the community in Harold's Cross: so many

The only surviving picture
of Anna Gaynor

died 'that graves had to be dug within the enclosure'. This, so rumour said, was to conceal behind its walls the deaths in the convent. In fact there were no deaths nor was there a graveyard 'within the enclosure'. In time there was built a side entrance to Mount Jerome Cemetery, which gate has not been used for three-quarters of a century. In the early days when consumption was killing one person every day in the Hospice, as an anonymous overestimate records, an adjacent graveyard was convenient. A discreet removal of remains from the mortuary at the back of the Hospice was less disturbing for the other patients but in practice most funerals went across the Liffey to Mount Prospect Cemetery in Glasnevin.

The Superior of the house in Harold's Cross at the time of the start of the Hospice was Anna Gaynor, known in religion as Mother Mary John. She had been secretary to the Superior in St Vincent's Hospital, M. Scholastica Margison, who in 1876 moved to Harold's Cross as Superior General; there Gaynor continued as her secretary.

Anna Gaynor's is a name still spoken of with respect in Harold's Cross. She was one of the five daughters of a Roscommon couple who had moved to a house in Belvedere Place, then the fashionable area in Dublin. Gaynor helped her parents in their visits to the starving and the sick in Roscommon—this was the time of Ireland's 'Great Hunger' and the epidemics of typhoid, cholera and typhus which accompanied the Famine. This interest in the suffering of others led Gaynor to join the Sisters of Charity; she made her professional vows in 1857. Anna Gaynor's qualities of charm and cheerfulness, her competence and her gift with the pen, her dedication to the religious life, ensured her succession to the post of Superior in Harold's Cross in the year the Hospice started in 1879. Aikenhead had died in 1858 but certainly knew Gaynor as a novice; that in Gaynor she discerned qualities of leadership seems highly probable, given that St Vincent's Hospital took first place in Aikenhead's affections and that the post of Secretary to this new and still growing hospital was an important one in which Anna Gaynor had been more than successful.

For a competent and business-like woman one surprising character trait of Anna Gaynor is that she was notoriously unpunctual. It is recorded with affectionate amusement:

> The one great difficulty Gaynor had to face daily and to fight against appears to have been a losing battle. Unpunctual she was at the start of her life and unpunctual she remained to the end. . . . This failing possibly endeared her all the more to her community because through this unpunctuality the Sisters experienced her need of them—many a soft tap on her door was needed to remind her of the next duty.

This cameo of personality was written in 1979 by Sister Katherine Butler[13] but is not mentioned in the Annals at the time of Gaynor's death, 80 years earlier—these refer to her 'great organising ability'. But the impact of folklore and tradition may be more vivid than any contemporary report.

The only extant first-hand accounts of the early days of Our Lady's Hospice date from the year after the Hospice started: the Annual Report for the year commencing September 1880. Bed numbers were 40, an increase from the initial 9; since its opening 336 patients had been admitted. There is an interesting comment about the relatively large sum spent on food: '[Our Lady's Hospice] is an expensive establishment because deathbeds [sic] especially in consumptive cases the appetite is rather augmented than diminished'. Increased appetite along with a false optimism about the future were known features of some cases of terminal tuberculosis.

There is another comment about the patients' diet which makes plain the difference between the Hospice and hospitals where people were not terminally ill. 'The dying cannot be treated as ordinary patients but must have the more expensive diet and treatment their exhausted condition requires.'

The 1883 and 1884 reports are noteworthy as the first to give financial details. Receipts at £775 were down because of a fall in donations and bequests. But a grant from the Dublin Corporation of £150 is mentioned; it had started at £100 and was to continue slowly to rise. The Rathmines and Rathgar Commissioners were to contribute smaller amounts.

A notebook listing all bequests from August of 1881 up to 1927 has survived. These show that for 1884 bequests were the major source of income: 87 per cent. This pattern was to continue for many years: charitable bequests were common in the wills of the well off. An example a few years later is £1,000 from James Scallan 'per Dr Walshe'. Now Walshe was the Catholic Archbishop of Dublin; he was the patron and friend of the Hospice and Scallan may have left the bequest at Walshe's discretion.

Sara Atkinson has been mentioned as the biographer of Aikenhead. In 1888 she produced a pamphlet about Our Lady's Hospice in which she writes, 'one thing at any rate is certain, the Irish as a rule know how to die'; this is praise indeed. A similar comment about the Hospice was made at that time in the USA by Rosa Mulholland, who wrote in the *Boston Pilot*: 'The Irish die more gladly than any other people upon earth.' The first less sweeping comment carries more conviction but clearly the atmosphere the Irish Sisters had created for the dying had much impressed both authors.

4 A new building

The original main house, Greenmount, is a large, three-storied, late-eighteenth-century building. As part of its pre-Hospice adaptation, a two-storied connecting building had provided a chapel, a refectory and cells or cubicles overhead for novices: these became a female ward (St Joseph's) with men downstairs in what was then called St Michael's. This meant 40 new beds. This bed complement in no way met the demand for admission and conditions were not ideal. A new purpose-built building had become essential. Funds were needed.

State medicine, social welfare: these and other economic factors have changed utterly the financing of what were once 'charitable institutions'. The motivation of charitable donors presupposes the desire to share their income with others. There are many such people still around today. Like other hospitals and hospices, Our Lady's Hospice relies heavily on the goodwill of its friends. A historian of medicine refers to 'bourgeois philanthropy' and attributes the nineteenth-century rise of the hospital to the increased social mobility which followed the growth of towns. He goes further: 'The pursuit of social status, by both patrons and doctors, becomes a key to the growth of hospitals.'[14] This is an interesting idea but one certain to be denied at the time by those mentioned. It is true that in those days doctors and lawyers were looked down upon by landowners and were parked in a slot little higher than shopkeepers. The lengthy lists of the names of those attending early fundraising events for Our Lady's Hospice were published in full in the newspapers of the day. These lists bristle with suffixes such as MP (Member of Parliament) or PC (Peace Commissioner) and titles like Councillor, Alderman, Honourable, Lady, etc. A strong sniff of snobbery comes through. In lists of donors the sum given is stated not only in newspapers but also in annual reports or in gilt lettering on a panel in the entrance hall of some hospitals.

There were gatherings of the affluent and the socially mobile in concert halls; charity sermons were preached in churches of different denominations. Today fashion shows, golf classics and coffee mornings are more popular and the total of donations is given but not individual amounts. Board members have replaced hospital governors, who often had the right to recommend admission. Such people do not just dispense their surplus funds but give freely of a more valuable commodity—time. In Our Lady's Hospice most of the facets mentioned above were in evidence.

The Corporation grant was now £250 annually (1886). Sponsorship of a bed cost £5 by which one became a 'Friend of the Hospice' and, if one wished, a brass plaque with the donor's name was hung over the bed.

The total sum from donors and subscribers that year was £535 and there was also, from Richard Devereux, a bequest of £1,000. But without another large bequest building could not begin. Such a bequest was on the way and may explain the date when foundation digging started.

Charles Hamill left to the Hospice a bequest of £8,000. He died in 1884 and his half-sister, Catherine, had the use of the bequest until her own death in 1886. Their gift is commemorated by a tablet over the entrance to the wing of the new building which is called 'St Charles Borromeo'. It is known as St Charles Ward to this day. That this bounty was not enough to fund all of the building, that the Hospice was in debt and that the Sisters still cheerfully proceeded with their plans comes as no surprise.

Public meetings for great causes were common in nineteenth-century Ireland. The politicians held them for Home Rule and meetings for charitable causes also raised money. The laying of the foundation stone for the new building was the occasion for a large

St Patrick's Ward (1899)—the dimity curtains were both practical and cheering.

gathering of the well-known in the grounds of the Hospice on Sunday 18 July 1886. After the blessing of the foundation stone by the Archbishop of Dublin the meeting was addressed from a stand in the field by Dublin's Lord Mayor John Redmond MP; William O'Brien, another nationalist MP, sent his apologies as did T. Harrington and T. D. Sullivan—all of these later sent subscriptions. The poet Katherine Tynan ('Sheep and Lambs') was there. The next day's newspapers gave a lengthy list of other guests and reported the speeches in many columns. A subscription list was opened and by that evening had reached £1,000. Whether it was appeals for funds, patriotic speeches or charity sermons, all these doings filled the papers of these days: 'the media' then had but one channel.

The new Hospice was designed by William R. Byrne and built by Richard Toole. Fronted with granite from Ballyknockan in Co. Wicklow, with limestone for the windows and front porch, from the outside it looks the same today. The rear wall is yellow brick from Co. Dublin. Three wards on each of the two main floors gave 110 new beds. The top storey was for staff. There were five rooms for private patients, probably in the wing called St Charles already mentioned. When the building was ready for use more than two years later it was reported that 'sanitation and ventilation, so important an adjunct, [for wards filled with cases of 'open', i.e. infectious tuberculosis] have been provided for on the most improved principles of science.'

Sometimes it is forgotten that 'science' did not start in the twentieth century. In this Victorian era the industrial revolution was changing both the workforce and men's ideas; new inventions and discoveries made for progress and there were great expectations that poverty and disease would be conquered. Belief in God was under attack by the evolutionists. The decline in the West of religious beliefs and practices was beginning, yet it was also the era of colonisation, of Christian missions to Africa and the East, of the ending of one kind of slavery and of social concern about working practices, poverty and disease. The foundations of scientific medicine were being laid in France, Germany, Britain and the USA. With this background it is no wonder that the nursing Sisters in Harold's Cross should talk about the 'principles of science' and that in an age of philanthropy it was possible to appeal successfully to the generosity of the wealthy. The Sisters had two other advantages: they were a new expanding and popular Order; above all they were Irish in a country ruled from London.

However, one of the earliest examples of charity for the Hospice gives the reverse side of the coin of alms-giving. A Miss Fitzgerald who was visiting the Hospice and walking down the avenue met another caller who was on her way to give 2s 6d to one of the Sisters who had looked after a relative. This chance meeting set Miss Fitzgerald thinking. She worked in Clery's, a large store in Dublin's O'Connell Street. There she began a regular collection of small sums from the other employees. Miss Fitzgerald eventually ended her days in the Hospice and before her death the sums collected by her and her colleagues totalled £2,000, all of this in copper coins—'the pennies of the poor'.

Another democratic and broadly-based form of charity was also the work of women: in a building in the grounds of the Hospice there met a sodality of the Children of Mary, run at the time by Sister Mary Eustace Eaton. She organised the girls as collectors for the Hospice. She did more: 'She organised a grand band of devoted men who for seventy years have tramped the streets, roads and lanes of Dublin gathering the money which the good citizens supply.' This work the men did on Sundays. In one year in the 1890s these 'Sunday collections' reached £505.

Charity sermons have been mentioned: two took place in Gardiner Street, the Jesuit church, and in Whitefriar Street, the Carmelite church. Both of these would have been regarded then as 'fashionable' places of worship. A sermon in Whitefriar Street by George Bruckridge SJ yielded £134. Another preacher was John P. Daly PP. One of the collectors at charity sermons, obviously a veteran in such matters, makes the interesting comment: 'Eloquence makes very little difference. We find that whoever is the preacher the result is almost always the same': a tribute to the congregation if not to the preacher.

In 1884 such a sermon saw £155 collected—this in a year when receipts generally were down due to a fall in donations and bequests. Subscriptions, however, those amounts collected by voluntary effort from Dublin's working people, kept their steady level of income for Our Lady's Hospice. The charity sermons continued certainly until 1920, probably longer, and they were reported at great length in the newspapers of the day.

From 1882 annual charity concerts were the other popular source of funds for the Hospice. The choice of music and venue is redolent of Dublin's past. In 1742 Handel conducted the first performance of his *Messiah* in Cassel's newly opened Music Hall in Fishamble Street. The proceeds of £400 went to two hospitals—Mercer's and the Charitable Infirmary in Jervis Street—and for the relief of prisoners. A century and a half later *The Messiah* remained a winner in the charity stakes, now held in the Antient [sic] Concert Rooms in Great Brunswick Street and for the benefit of Our Lady's Hospice. This venue later became famous for the first production of Yeats' *Countess Cathleen* in 1899, a play that met much clerical condemnation at the time. Later again there were Joycean associations with the Antient Concert Rooms. From its foundation the Hospice has been an intimate part of the history of Dublin City: helping the poor with the aid of the well-off—with style.

Following the completion of the new building there was a debt of £230. This had happened before and would again. Construction had taken just three years, not a long time for an age when energy meant muscle not machinery. By 1889 'after a delay there are 108 beds now in use'. The 'delay' referred to was due to a lack of funds which caused a brief stoppage in building, soon resumed with the aid of an anonymous donation. Until a second new building was added in 1962 the bed complement in Our Lady's Hospice changed very little—in 1936 it was 114.

For the first time we learn a very little about wages and salaries: A pharmacist and two medical officers together earned £346; there are no details of the respective salaries. Probably their work was part-time.

The Hospice for the Dying remained true to its name. In Ireland death meant wakes: the bereaved and their friends gathered together to mourn and to celebrate the move to eternity. Wakes conjure up visions of clay pipes and tobacco, of firkins of stout and jars of whiskey. But if your relative died in the Hospice things were different. Removal of the dead to a house, lodging or church was too expensive. Burial from the mortuary avoided what was called 'take and wake'. In the Roman Catholic Church priests and bishops had thundered from the pulpit about this bacchanalian tradition—without effect. More delicately the Sisters in Harold's Cross make the same point: 'The Hospice affords both directly and indirectly a check to the pernicious custom of wakes . . . Patients express satisfaction that the disreputable wake is sure to be avoided.'

But it would be very surprising if in some cases the dead were not honoured in the traditional way in some private or public house.

That wakes still took place is shown by this item from the Annals of the early 1890s. Mary Anne was a patient in the Hospice and 'against advice' had acquired two false teeth. After her death, wake and burial a neighbour came to enquire if the two false teeth had been removed before she was taken from the Hospice. The neighbour's worry was due to a firmly held belief that 'nobody with anything false about them will ever see the face of God'.

One last point about funerals. For many years most funerals left the Hospice by the side gate, that opening onto Greenmount Avenue. The front avenue was reserved for the cortèges of the wealthy, few though they were. This may have been in keeping with the social conscience and the customs of the day but strikes a harsh note in present times. The report in the Annals for 1947–53 continues: 'This practice gave offence to many and was the cause of much criticism. One of the reasons was the narrowness of the front avenue.' This had been widened already and in 1940 it was then widened again by moving back the railings on the left hand side at a cost of £482. From then on all funerals left by the same front avenue. The comment of the Chaplain of the time was 'Reverend Mother is broadening her outlook'.

5 Consolidation and continuity 1888–1914

The quarter of a century between the opening of the new building and the First World War were quiet years for the Hospice: no major changes, no crises, a steady flow of admissions, three-quarters of them still tuberculous. Treatment remained palliative.

As one would expect, the Annals of the Sisters of Charity concentrate on matters religious and the successions to the office of Superior and Mother General. The daily grind of nursing care, catering, housekeeping and administration is never mentioned—it is taken for granted. There are some snippets of information however and these follow.

Not all of the patients were poverty stricken; there is a note that 'Protestants, professors of Irish and French, doctors, solicitors, soldiers, sailors and members of every class and grade of society have come under the mantle of the Blessed Mother of God.'

Of particular concern to all who worked in Our Lady's Hospice was the illness of its first Superior, Anna Gaynor, who was forced to retire in August 1897, after seventeen years in charge. She died eighteen months later. Her secretary Sister Calasanctius Ingoldsby died within a short time of Gaynor and is credited with being 'one of the best accountants in the congregation'.

Gaynor's successor, Agnes Gertrude Chamberlain, left the Hospice in 1908 to become Superior General in the head house in Milltown, an event recorded in the Annals as 'the dreaded blow of her departure'. Her silver jubilee as a member of the Order had been celebrated the previous year and included a concert and a party for the collectors of alms for the Hospice. This 'thank you' party was held in St Laurence's, a large 'Instruction Room' often used for plays and concerts. It had a balcony and was beside the refectory; today this is the room near the entrance to the Chapel. Chamberlain had 'ruled with firm and gentle sway'. During her reign the north cloister had been added to the Chapel. She is commemorated by the Lourdes Grotto, still standing in the grounds—when built it lay on the boundary of the pasture field.

In the year 1896 there was published in a periodical called *The Lady of the House* a series about Dublin charities by an anonymous correspondent. An article about Our Lady's Hospice mentions that 'as yet the Sisters have not acquired a special wing for cancer'. The writer remarks that some patients go to St Vincent's Hospital for convalescence; a century later the notion that St Vincent's might be used as a convalescent home would cause outrage and amusement. A few other details from the same article are worth quoting; they have the flavour of an era long gone.

> In the wards are four-poster curtained iron beds [covered by] the freshest and cheeriest pink and white dimity. The open fire is never without a singing kettle, for hot water jars and soothing drinks are in demand all day . . . Men enjoy the use of a large smoking room in the evenings [and there is also] a smoking pavilion in the grounds in a sunny spot.

The pavilion just described is the one in 'the nuns' garden' to this day: its use has changed.

During the early years of the twentieth century the names of various visitors to the Hospice are mentioned: Cardinal Moran from Sydney, the English Jesuit Bernard Vaughan who introduced the wife of the Lord Lieutenant Lady Dudley—she came twice. Every female patient got a bunch of flowers when Queen Alexandra paid a visit.

Far more important than visits by royalty or church dignitaries are people who 'visited' the Hospice as their last abode. The annual admission figures for these years were in the mid-300s and, as mentioned, most had tuberculosis. The preponderance of men continued. Both these statistics would change with the First World War. The average stay before death was just three months and the number of deaths each year at this time ranged from 204 to 344 for the years 1890 to 1903.

It is surprising to some that in a Hospice for the dying a fair number of patients just left: about one-third of them in the period under discussion. From the same wards today, in what is now the Extended Care Unit, discharges are almost unknown but the reason for the contrast is clear: patients dying from incurable tuberculosis and other fatal diseases compared to the slow decline that is old age.

Why people left Our Lady's Hospice in those very different times is a matter for conjecture. The admission books of that era list in the single narrow column headed 'Results' the laconic statements 'Died (date)', 'Left', 'Discharged' or 'Dismissed'. The precise meaning of the last three types of 'Results' can only be guessed at. The category 'Dismissed' includes but a very small number of patients and may mean discharge for disciplinary reasons. 'Left' suggests they took their own discharge for personal or family reasons, while others were judged improved enough to be 'Discharged' home. Like many words in the language their meaning may have changed over the generations and these interpretations given a century later are no more than current hospital usage.

A better comparison than the modern Extended Care Unit for those leaving Our Lady's Hospice in the early 1900s is the Palliative Care Unit: there in 1997 20 per cent were discharged as against 33 per cent in the Hospice of 1897 and readmissions to the Palliative Care Unit are quite common. Some want to die at home among their own, as was the case in the early days of Our Lady's Hospice. Although there are no figures for readmission in the sparse records of the early days the impression is that such numbers were very small.

However, one important reason that many of these people left Our Lady's Hospice is to be found in the reason for their admission

Back view of the Hospice (1890s)—tubercular patients taking the air on the balcony.

in the first place: they were taken in, not because of fatal illness, but rather because of starvation, poverty and helplessness. This is in keeping with the motivation for the founding of the Hospice and with the ethos of the Sisters of Charity. It was they who visited the tenements, sought out the needy and made sure they were seen by the admitting doctor. Occasionally in the registers in the column headed 'Referred by' one sees not a medical name but that of a Sister from another institution—there were then a dozen other RSC convents, schools and orphanages in Dublin alone: the Sisters working there were a source of referrals to Our Lady's Hospice.

There may have been then no extensions to the Hospice buildings but the entrance was improved and widened: the old iron gate was 'replaced by one at once handsome and simple' and the pillars and surrounds were now of granite. This work, along with a separate entrance for the school, cost £450. Also of practical importance was the installation of electric light for £300. The type of generator or power supply is not given; it was not water driven by the small

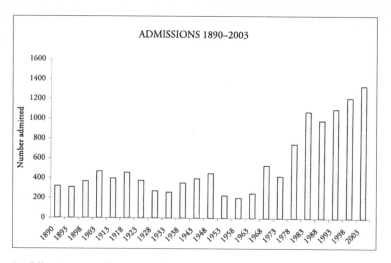

ADMISSIONS 1890–2003

Poddle River in the grounds.

A link with Ireland's past is mentioned in the Annals of these times. 'A sullen reserved man' was admitted: he died peacefully. He had spent fifteen years in gaol for killing a policeman, an activity commoner then than now. He was said to be connected with 'the Invincibles' that oath-bound secret society responsible for the Phoenix Park murders when Cavendish and Burke, the Chief and Under Secretaries in the UK's Irish administration, were stabbed to death in 1882.

In Ireland at large these early years of the twentieth century were exciting times: Sinn Féin founded, the Big Strike of 1913; the passage of the Home Rule Bill, the Ulster and then the Irish and the National Volunteers began enrolment; gun-running in Larne and Howth. The long-expected world war came in August of 1914 and 'the lights began to go out all over Europe'. In Harold's Cross the care of the dying continued unchanged.

6 Early medical staff and patient care

Dudley White was the first medical man to serve the Hospice and his death in December 1895 after sixteen years of service is recorded in the Annals. White had qualified in 1866 from the Royal College of Surgeons in Ireland and would have been about 36 years of age when the Hospice opened. Like his father, White was City Coroner and he was also in charge of the North City Dispensary. We get a glimpse of the character of the man in this appreciation by one of the Sisters: 'Dr Dudley White had a bright and cheery manner which endeared him to all patients, especially to the young to whom he brought sweets or perhaps a paper or a book.'

After White information in the Annals is conspicuous by its absence until 1945 when a list of doctors is mentioned by Katherine Butler;[13] surnames only are given and there are no dates. Recourse to medical registers and directories and that mine of information *Thoms' Directory* has provided a few additional facts. A late find was an album of press cuttings (1900–21) rescued by Gary Redmond; this gave some more material. At the suggestion of Tony Farmar the Kirkpatrick collection in the College of Physicians yielded some further facts.

Michael Strahan was a demonstrator in anatomy at the Cecilia Street School of Medicine in Dublin, which was part of Newman's Catholic University in St Stephen's Green. He qualified in Dublin (LRCSI 1863) and Edinburgh (LRCPEd. 1865) and at one time ran a general practice in Rutland (now Parnell) Square in Dublin; this was Number 2 Dispensary District of the North Dublin Union. He is listed as an attending physician to Our Lady's Hospice in 1904 and remained as such until his death in 1908.

Garret Waters Joyce, like his contemporary Strahan, attended Cecilia Street and also the older Carmichael School. He qualified LRCPI in 1890 and practised in Leinster Road, Rathmines, and is listed as attending Our Lady's Hospice from 1896 to 1915. Like all the other doctors mentioned here he was a general practitioner, a custom which is continued to this day in the Medical Directors of the Extended Care Unit. But Joyce was also Cardiologist to Hume Street Hospital and became a Fellow of the Royal College of Surgeons in Ireland (FRCSI). Later he was made a Justice of the Peace in Rathfarnham: clearly he was a man of parts.

Family doctors were called 'physicians' or 'physicians and surgeons' for many years. A visiting physician was more specialised in his interests and usually was on the staff of a hospital or more often several hospitals. Such a man was Michael Francis Cox from Co. Roscommon who was attached to St Vincent's Hospital. He was also the solitary Consultant Physician to the Hospice. Cox had two unique milestones in his career. In 1911 he was the first practising physician to be appointed to the Privy Council of the UK. He did more: he resigned from the Council in 1920 in protest at Lloyd George's policy in Ireland—the use of curfew, martial law, the 'Black and Tans', the 'Auxiliary' force and other measures to combat the Irish Republican Army. That Cox was often called to see patients in Our Lady's Hospice is unlikely. He is named on the list of staff from 1891 to 1915.

Robert Percy McDonnell worked alongside Joyce in the Hospice to which he was appointed in 1908. Born in 1876 McDonnell came from Co. Roscommon. His career is interesting. Serving in the British Army he was present at the battle of Omdurman in the Sudan in 1898; now a captain in the medical corps (RAMC) he saw action in the Boer War and in the First World War at Gallipoli with the Irish Division. When the Free State was founded he became a colonel in the newly formed 'Irish National Medical Service' [sic]. McDonnell had studied medicine in Cecilia Street and qualified LRCP & SI in 1901, proceeding to the surgical Fellowship in 1903. Later he took a

Male patients' sitting room (1909)

Diploma in Public Health and became Deputy and then Chief Adviser to the Department of Health. For how long he continued to attend at the Hospice is not known, but it is certain that he did so from 1908 to 1915; he may have resumed his Hospice work after his RAMC service. Unlike others among the doctors in earlier times in the Hospice we do know his salary: £100 per annum. After this multifaceted career he died aged 74 years in 1950.

Joseph Daniel was another Cecilia Street and Catholic University man, taking his medical qualification from the College of Physicians and Surgeons in 1906; this was the normal practice until the foundation of the National University of Ireland in 1907 when University College Dublin succeeded Newman's College; it now had the power to grant medical degrees. Daniel was the Chief Tuberculosis Officer for Dublin until 1947, a post complementing his clinical work with the consumptive patients in the Hospice. He died in 1951.

Fergus Shiel worked in the Hospice from 1953 to 1954. He had graduated from NUI (UCD) in 1948 but soon left Dublin to become a pathologist in Virginia, USA.

Patrick Alphonsus O'Callaghan qualified LRCP & SI in 1948

and set up a general practice in Blessington Street. Later he became District Medical Officer in Dundrum. He joined Fleetwood as attending physician to the Long Stay Unit about 1963 and worked there until 1990 when he retired after nearly 30 years' service.

Michael J. Mullen is the first medical graduate of the new National University of Ireland to attend the Hospice. He qualified in 1930 and worked in Harold's Cross in the 1940s and 50s. His work was that of all his predecessors: the care of the bed-bound and the dying.

Patrick T. J. O'Farrell wrote a vivid account of his work in the Hospice which is quoted later. He qualified from the Colleges of Physicians and Surgeons in 1910 and, like his predecessors, had attended Cecilia Street; the religious divide then between Catholic and Protestant in Ireland included medical schools and hospital appointments and was to last until ecumenism prevailed in more recent times. O'Farrell was a visiting physician to St Vincent's Hospital in Dublin where his older brother Thomas T. O'Farrell was the pathologist and also Professor in University College Dublin.

The remaining three names on the 1945 list are Drs Fagan, Keegan and Kennedy, about whom information is lacking, but for the last half-century we are on sure ground about the Hospice doctors. Their names are to be found in the accounts of the three units of the Hospice, but in this case I have refrained from giving an invidious list of all their degrees, fellowships and distinctions.

Spiritual care is well covered in the Annals of the Sisters of Charity and has been dealt with in detail in other published accounts.[9, 12, 13] In medical care the regime of daily dosing and hygiene, of inhalers and soporifics are nowhere documented. An occasional doctor is mentioned, but neither Sister nor nurse numbers are anywhere to be found. Domestic staff likewise. The only exception to this reticence about staff numbers is a single statement referring apparently to the 1890s: 'One nun with one maid ran each ward.'

Were there any what are now called paramedical assistants, male orderlies or porters? Did relatives of the dying do more than sit and watch and wait for the end? It is on record that they brought gifts to their friends and had access to a kettle on the hob.

Educated guesses about treatment may be made from the medical mores of the time. Digitalis for heart failure, morphine and aspirin for pain: these drugs then stood alone as effective medicines for serious complaints. Purgatives for constipation abounded as did tonics for tiredness and anaemia, despite the lack of iron in many of these elixirs. 'Stimulants' included strychnine and spirits; alcohol's value lay in its pain-relieving and sedative powers which was one reason why tinctures—alcoholic solutions—of drugs of varying kinds were so popular with both doctors and patients. Surgery was in its infancy as was anaesthesia—operations would have been of little use for the dying patients in the Hospice. This meagre summary is put more succinctly in the Annals in 1888: 'The kindly doctor takes his daily round exhausting the resources of his science in procuring alleviation for one and all.'

We do know from what most of these patients suffered: tuberculosis. In leather-bound ledgers are listed names, addresses, referring doctors and diagnoses on admission. The admissions and the numbers of tuberculosis and cancer patients are shown on page 53. For both these diseases there was palliative care, but no cure. The use of this term 'palliative care' came into vogue three-quarters of a century after Our Lady's Hospice's foundation, but it was practised from the beginning—within the limits of knowledge of the time.

What may surprise some is the resistance to the idea that tuberculosis was an infectious disease. It was supposed by many to be hereditary. It was associated with poverty and was a socially unacceptable condition not to be mentioned in polite circles. In the Registrar General's classification of disease and mortality, tuberculosis was not listed among the fatal fevers such as smallpox, measles or typhoid, nor had Dublin Corporation recognised it as a notifiable disease requiring isolation or quarantine. This was not to happen for many years. Even then the regulations were not enforced until 1911 and were often ignored.

For the first two decades of Our Lady's Hospice's existence deaths from tuberculosis nation-wide continued to rise. With no available treatment, somewhere to die in the comfort of a warm bed and a benign atmosphere made Harold's Cross a much sought refuge for those with terminal tuberculosis. The alternative to dying at home was a sanatorium, but as late as 1914 there were in all Ireland only 900 such beds available, these scattered among general and work-house hospitals and a few sanatoriums. These patients were young people—the first admission was a student sixteen years of age. The average age at which tuberculosis proved fatal was then under 30 years of age. The ages of inmates at this time confirm the national figures. Naturally enough the story of that first admission to Our Lady's Hospice has been told more than once in the Annals and elsewhere[12] and is retold now.

'Like many a medical student before him Joseph Sharkey had been very wild'—this is the popular view of doctors-to-be. Sharkey was Irish yet owed his admission to his English brother-in-law who importuned the Sisters to give him a bed—there had been rumours that a hospice was to open in Harold's Cross. He was lucky: the day he called was a Sunday and higher authority in the person of the Superior General of the Order was in the house and Sharkey was admitted as the first patient on the next day, 16 September 1879. He died six weeks later.

A final word about Sharkey. He was said to be aged sixteen: students were able to join a medical school at a younger age in those days. The Annals of the time describe him as follows: 'The poor fellow had become wild like many others of his age. He was a fine young man full of spirits and of hope . . . he had come for a while to get well.'

As a classical case history of terminal tuberculosis this account could not be bettered: the age, the 'wild life', the undimmed hope of a cure, the speedy end. Joe Sharkey was to be the first of many like him.

Apart from Sharkey we do know a little about the other early arrivals: making up the nucleus of nine patients were a young carpenter, an older man, a boy, a shoemaker, a governess, two servants and an elderly woman who was a roomkeeper—a spectrum of society and generations.

The extant Registers of Admissions start in 1893. In that year 77 per cent of the 305 admissions had tuberculosis. More men than women had this disease. As the bar chart shows, 25 years later at the end of First World War this proportion was maintained. Then began the steady decline in tuberculosis admissions, a fall which preceded the advent of antibiotics and new sanitoriums—it was a natural and national decline. The 1950s saw the arrival of these new drugs and of more sanitoriums and these eliminated tuberculosis as a reason for admission to Our Lady's Hospice. An era had ended. One surprising fact in the admission statistics of OLH in the early years is the preponderance of men among the tuberculosis patients (see page 42). It is known that under 35 years of age it was women who were more at risk. The reasons for this anomaly are uncertain. Later the bed accommodation favoured women but was this Hospice policy rather than a reaction to demand? In general it is true that women are more likely to seek admission for any complaint.

At present in the long-stay wards women still predominate: life expectancy favours females. In the arthritis unit the much larger number of women is explained by the commonest disease treated there—rheumatoid arthritis: the usual male to female ratio for this disease is as one is to three.

Returning to the earlier years the non-tuberculous minority suffered from the expected complaints: heart disease, stroke, joint disease, tumours. Leg ulcers are mentioned, as are gout and kidney stones. One must remember that the nature and cause of many diseases had yet to be discovered: diabetes for example, rheumatic and coronary heart disease, vitamin deficiencies, the causes of anaemia and many others. Chest x-rays were not used in Our Lady's Hospice for at least half a century, nor were laboratory tests available—these advances did not come until the 1930s.

The long corridor in the 1940s

Early patient records or charts do not exist. Dr John Fleetwood was Ireland's first geriatrician, i.e. a physician specialising in the care of older people. He was appointed to Our Lady's Hospice in 1961 and has written about the Long Stay Unit as he found it:[16]

> Many if not most of the patients were long-stay cases with social as much as medical problems. . . . The importance of relieving troublesome as distinct from painful symptoms could be overlooked. There were practically no clinical records. The internationally-recommended patient to nurse ratio in geriatric units was two to one but was five to one at Our Lady's Hospice.

[But] when at my invitation the British Geriatric Society visited Dublin in 1963 they were amazed at the volume and quality of the nursing provided in the Hospice.

Fleetwood examined the reasons for admission to Our Lady's Hospice. From the answers given by the families of the patients he concluded that

> . . . improved domiciliary care services would have reduced or delayed the number of long-term admissions, thus allowing more of the terminally ill to be admitted—the type of patient for whom Our Lady's Hospice was founded.

This comment is still applicable to many admissions to Our Lady's Hospice but domiciliary care became common practice only in the next 30 years.

7 Wars at home and abroad 1914–1922

The First World War had started and soon there were to be wars in Ireland, called at the time with our usual euphemism 'The Troubles'. References to the fighting are few in the Annals but are of interest.

One of the Irish Volunteers involved in the 1916 Rising died in the Hospice. He was aged 20 years and

> . . . had caught a cold during the rebellion. His funeral was a sight for Ireland. The tricolour covered his coffin and the trams [which passed the gate of the Hospice] all stopped for his funeral. Several photographers rang up to know if they might take photos of the procession.

Such consideration is not seen among the paparazzi of today.

Years later another Volunteer of those times was to die in the Hospice. His funeral from there was attended by the Taoiseach, Ministers and Members of the Dáil. Margaret Pearse was present. This Galway man was Barney Mellowes, brother of Liam who had been executed in 1922.

In the Hospice arguments about politics or religion were not encouraged by the Sisters, but the writer of the notes about the Sodality does not hide her national views:

> [We] avoided politics and taking sides as much as possible although our Celtic much-wronged feelings have to be curbed. Keeping in mind the merciful universal Redemption we cannot forget those whose cruel tyranny goads our people. So the terrible onslaught of detested spies is bought by the same Precious Blood [of Christ].

National feelings were nothing new in Our Lady's Hospice. In

Edwardian times a dying Wexford man got his two sons to make a bedside promise 'that come what may they would never wear the red coat [of the British Army]'.

It is quite certain that the Sisters during these times prayed for the welfare of the dead on all sides during the First World War, the War of Independence and the Civil War. Above all they prayed for peace.

There were many more placid events in the Hospice at this time. The first was the celebration in 1915 of the Centenary of the Religious Sisters of Charity. High Mass was said. The Artane Boys' Band arrived in a special tram and 'discoursed delightful selections'. Less happy was a rainstorm on 19 November. The Dodder river burst not only its banks but also the dam at Boharnabreena. Of more import to the Hospice was the overflowing of the Poddle which is connected to the Dodder by a man-made stream. The Poddle is a tributary of the Liffey and runs a strange, often underground, course. It has now been built over for most of its length. In 1915 it ran through the grounds of the Hospice and was bridged by the avenue. The flooding reached the school but not the higher-lying Hospice. Next door in the houses in Greenmount Lane the occupants had to leave by the top windows. Pumping by the fire brigade did not alter the levels of water, which took three days to subside. Similar flooding by the Poddle happened again in 1930: this time twenty girls and women from the same neighbouring houses were given lodging in the Hospice. The Poddle was diverted and covered over in 1991 and the avenue bridge disappeared.

In the summer of 1920 at the height of the War of Independence and the curfew, a garden fête was planned to raise funds. A downpour of rain turned the field into a quagmire but undaunted the fête went ahead. 'The ballroom was crowded each evening. There were concerts, bands, people promenading and enjoying themselves.' Beside Robert Emmet Bridge over the Canal, a couple of hundred yards from the Hospice, there was and is a long-established fuel merchant called Gordon's. In those days much fuel was transported by horse-drawn or motor-driven barges. Mr P. Gordon ran motor barges to and from St James's Harbour beside the brewery during the ten days of the fête. In all £4,000 went to the Hospice.

A letter written to the UK Government during 'the Troubles' of 1920 was not inspired by the shootings or explosions. It is a good example of the many appeals for funds being made by hospices and hospitals over tens of decades. The letter highlights the problems of that era before the socialisation of medicine. It is well worth quoting in full, replete as it is with the facts and figures so necessary for a letter to the civil service or local government. The failure of a promised grant to materialise strikes a familiar chord today.

4th May 1920

Re : eight hours' day for Nurses.

Dear Sir,

In reply to your communication of April 20th, I beg to say that it would be necessary for us to close down one third of the Hospice to comply with your request [for the implementation of an eight hour day for nurses]. *[i]*

We have no accommodation for more nurses and our financial position is overstrained to the utmost to meet the ever increasing cost of provisions.

Besides your grant our only fixed income from other sources amounts to £454 per annum—in 1914 the expenditure was £6,207.5.10, whilst in 1919 it has raised to £10,253.6.3, making an increase of £4,000 in our current expenditure.

Our patients with very few exceptions being the very poor of the City cannot afford to contribute to their maintenance; during the past week the contributions of patients (exclusive of payments made for discharged soldiers & of tubercular patients from the County Insurance Committees) amounted to £6.10.0.

We are excluded from payment for old age pensioners, of whom we have at present 27, we are also, though approved by the Local Government Board, excluded by the Corporation from payment for tubercular patients from the City, of whom we have at present 17.

Under these circumstances you will understand the impossibility of adding one third of our nursing staff, which would be necessary given an 8 hours' day unless indeed the Corporation on its side can proportionately increase the grant and can also agree to make an adequate payment for insured and non-insured patients from the City.

The 'eight hour day' was never implemented in full.

There is a good story about a bookmaker named Mickey who spent his last days in the Hospice at this time. According to the Annals he had 'led a very dissipated life. A great many visitors came to see him, all bringing the little drop to keep up his spirits'. There is no mention that Mickey continued to take bets from patients or visitors. Before he died, reconciled to his Maker, another patient said, 'When we go up to Heaven we'll be asked to take our place in the queue but when Mickey goes up there they will clap their hands and cheer "Here he comes at last!"'

Mention of bookmakers suggests the greyhound track up the road in Harold's Cross. For some the words 'Harold's Cross' mean not the Hospice but this stadium run by the Dublin Greyhound Racing Association (DGRA). The DGRA was generous in their annual donation to the Hospice for most of a century; contributors included administrators, bookmakers and the 'punters'—the folk whose entrance fees and wagers keep the DGRA in being. The Hospice, like most hospitals in Ireland, did not regard it as morally wrong to profit from gambling; when the Sweepstakes started in the 1930s this was the reason given by some voluntary hospitals for refusing such funding—in fact retention of independence of government grants was the more likely reason.

On a more mundane level, the brick frontage of the old Big House was cemented over. Water pipes were renewed, the laundry extended and 'all necessary appliances, electrical and otherwise, were updated'. More importantly a qualified nurse was assigned to each ward, this in addition to the RSC Sisters already in post; this increase in nursing staff took place in the early 1920s. During these

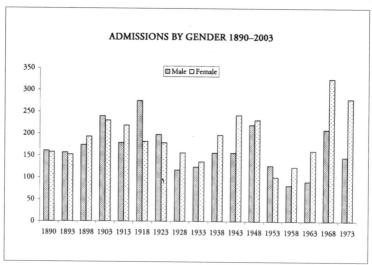

ADMISSIONS BY GENDER 1890–2003

□ Male □ Female

1890 1893 1898 1903 1913 1918 1923 1928 1933 1938 1943 1948 1953 1958 1963 1968 1973

times mention is made again of a new cancer ward, 'an ardent hope, a long felt want'. Evidence of these hopes is seen in the list of donors in 1919: the large sum of £500 sterling was the 'Bequest of Mr A. Heagh decd., per A. Heagh, towards proposed Cancer Wing'. Later two other members of the Heagh family also left bequests for this purpose. It was to be more than 40 years before these hopes were realised.

8 Continuing care and upkeep 1923–1959

During these times there is a report of 'a fine new hayshed' and the dairy acquired an electric motor—the Shannon Hydro-Electric Scheme (now the ESB) had started in 1929. A poultry farm is mentioned. New iron railings surrounded the front field and the gravel of the avenue was replaced by concrete—an interesting detail related to the newly started home production of cement.

Things eternal were not forgotten: a Lourdes Grotto for Our Lady was built and presented by the school's staff and pupils: this Marian School was in the grounds of the Hospice to the left of the avenue. For the Eucharistic Congress in Dublin in 1932 loudspeakers were installed in the grounds to relay the new national radio station in Athlone. There was another speaker inside at the Chapel door: a good choice from which to broadcast the commentary down 'the long corridor' of the main building. Seventy years later this same corridor has become over 100 yards in length—'long' indeed.

Beside the Chapel there was a vegetable garden described by a Sister as 'disreputable'. It was replaced by a rose garden, still blooming in 2004. Here too are glasshouses supplying flowers and potted plants for the Chapel and wards.

A 'new byre for kine' cost £2,000 and the pigs were rehoused. Replacement of that essential hospital item, the laundry, became necessary; the new boiler house and chimney cost £8,000 and the boiler house is still in use 60 years later—naturally with some changes and now fuelled by natural gas instead of oil or coal. Expenditure demands income and for the first time there was a new source: the Hospitals Sweepstakes, that lottery on horse racing that took place thrice a year. In the 1930s 'The Sweep', as it was known, had written off the Hospice deficit, now a building grant was applied for—what building was intended is not specified. The Second World War put a halt to the Sweep and to these plans.

Éire was a neutral country during the Second World War: the Government labelled this precarious time 'the Emergency'. But work was available in the factories in England and the armed forces of the United Kingdom were happy to take volunteers from any part of the island of Ireland. Beef and butter exports to the UK soared despite German submarine warfare which had escalated in 1941. All of these factors led to a rise in prosperity in Ireland: the 30s and 50s compare poorly with conditions during the Second World War, but rationing of tea, butter, oil and coal were a fact of life and affected Dublin in particular. Along with the rest of the capital city, Our Lady's Hospice had contacts and friends in the better supplied countryside. Whether convents or other contacts, whether friends of the staff or the relatives of patients, all these people remembered Dublin during 'the Emergency'. It may have been only a trickle of rationed goods but its value in boosting morale far outweighed this supplement to the wartime diet. Any Dublin senior citizen will remember with joy the arrival from the country of the turkey for Christmas.

Fear of air raids grew after the fall of France in 1940. Shelters were built and the windows in the Hospice were wired and 'cellophane pasted on sheet glass'. When in 1941 three German bombs fell in Terenure, just a mile way, 20 windows were broken; the glass fragments fell outside and there were no casualties. The school building was sandbagged. The only mention of food shortages or rationing is the report that the Rectress of the time, Lelia Butler, had laid in stores of food.

Complaints are not a feature of the Annals. The Hospice in Harold's Cross was unique among wartime Dublin hospitals in having within its grounds home-grown supplies of milk, butter, eggs and bacon to meet some of the demands of more than 200 people. Ground at the rear became a fruit garden as imports of fruit

A newspaper advertisment showing fundraising 1920s style

had ceased. Most of the orchard had been cut down at the time of the new building in 1886. The gardener then was Tom Brazil, who had wept real tears at the felling of his trees.

During the Second World War admissions rose by 10–15 per cent and continued to rise until 1948 when the figure was 451 patients—the highest number since the end of the First World War. Nation-wide as well as world-wide there was an increase in the incidence of tuberculosis during and after both wars, a rise not mirrored in Our Lady's Hospice; in fact there was a fall of 6 per cent in the relative numbers of tuberculosis patients. This cannot be explained by the arrival of new sanatorium beds or curative drugs. One reason may have been the emigration of young workers to Britain; in that country the wartime rise in tuberculosis was greater than in Ireland. The explanation of the big rise of 22 per cent in total admissions over the decade to 1948 is harder to explain; there was no increase in bed numbers in Our Lady's Hospice, no pandemic of influenza as at the end of the First World War. Figures are hypnotic and all of us labour under the tyranny of numbers: let us accept that we cannot always explain the reasons behind percentages.

The period after the Second World War, especially the 1950s, were times of economic depression and shortage of funds for national development. Undaunted, a new nurses' home, St Michael's, was built. Money might be short but building materials had become available again. St Michael's lies near the St Charles wing of the main building and is parallel to it. Local fund-raising for this consisted of weekly concerts on Sunday nights organised by Myles Breslin. The actors gave their services free. They took place in the Carnegie Hall of the school, within the grounds of Our Lady's Hospice. Andrew Carnegie was a Scotsman from Dunfermline who made a large fortune in the USA. After his death much of his money recrossed the Atlantic to build libraries and halls, not just in Scotland but throughout Ireland and elsewhere.

Not only concerts but also a four-week long carnival in the summer of 1948 were organised. The carnival alone made a profit of £7,000 and there was a grant of £16,000 from the revised Sweepstake Funds. There were radio appeals e.g. by Frank Hugh O'Donnell; much later there was an RTE appeal by Gay Byrne who also hosted the televised 'Light up a Life' event (see later). A more durable gift was that of a statue of Our Lady of Fatima given by the busmen of the national transport company, Coras Iompair Eireann (CIE), in 1948. This had been organised by one of their staff, Ronnie Kelly, who had been a patient in the Hospice. The statue is of white marble and for many years was covered in white paint. It stood in a stone grotto at the top of the avenue. A plaque commemorates the generosity of the CIE men who gave it in gratitude for the care by the Hospice of their workmates. More recently, car park extensions and a new ESB sub-station involved moving the statue nearer to the Chapel and there building a new base of boulders along with curtain walls. As well as its intended function it serves to mask the utility behind it. Now on its new site and with the layers of paint removed, the fine carving in the marble is again apparent; the sculptor is not known.

Nineteen-fifty-eight was the centenary of Mary Aikenhead's death. Harold's Cross, as the mother house from which she controlled the Order's expansion and the place where she died, headed the celebration. A play written by Sister Alphonsus Bailey Butler was broadcast by Radio Éireann. As with many Dublin events of any note, the Artane Boys' Band marched and played. High Mass was notable for the sermon of Monsignor O'Halloran from Glasthule; his were the thought-provoking words that Aikenhead 'had done more for Ireland than Daniel O'Connell', her contemporary, the national politician who among other things had won Catholic Emancipation allowing entry to parliament for the non-established faiths.

The decade of the 1950s was significant in another way: it saw the admission of the last case of tuberculosis to the Hospice, a lone male patient in 1958. The torrent of such cases in the early years had gradually subsided and now ceased. This had taken three-quarters of a century. Patients with cancer made up one-third of the total in that same year, a proportion only barely exceeded after the Palliative Care Unit opened 25 years later. The other major point was the fall in admissions; half the number of a decade earlier, when nearly one-third of the patients had tuberculosis. A change in Hospice

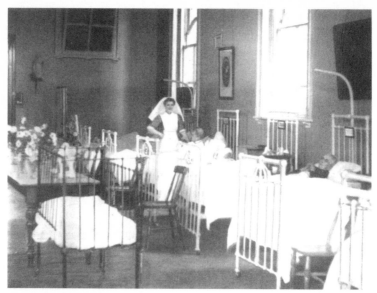

St Mary's Ward in the 1940s

policy was needed. There is a note in the Annals that 'the new extension would cost £60,000'. This refers to the new unit—St Joseph's, which was to open in 1961 and will be discussed in the next section.

One small but revealing note in the Annals in these post-war years was the recording of the unexpected visit to the Hospice of the Papal Nuncio, a gentleman with the very Irish name of Gerald P. O'Hara. One result of his visit was 'his request that for three days the Sisters were to get more sleep and that talking was permitted everywhere except in the Chapel'. Personal austerity was still the rule.

9 Staff reminiscences from mid-century

Personal experience of a workplace, however it may be remembered, sheds more light than many a second-hand account or annual report. Some retired members of the staff of Our Lady's Hospice have been good enough to write of their memories of the Hospice. The following are a few of their reminisces, quoted verbatim.

Margaret Prendergast was Pharmacist to Our Lady's Hospice for 30 years, working alongside her husband Frank. It is Hospice folklore that when the stock of morphine mixture became out of date Mrs Prendergast used it to water her potted plants. They thrived.

She writes (29 November 2001):

> My abiding memory of the Hospice in Harold's Cross, is the dedication of the Religious Sisters to the sick and dying.
>
> I saw the Sisters eat dry bread on Fridays and they certainly had no luxuries of any kind. Everything they had was for the patients. They were on duty and in the wards from early morning until ten o'clock at night, with no time off except for prayer. No waste of any kind was permitted. Every empty box and jar had to be salvaged.
>
> The spirituality and prayerfulness of the Sisters seemed to seep from the building, so it was a very special place. I went there reluctantly for a few weeks just to cover until a new pharmacist was appointed: I stayed 30 years. This was the story of so many employees who worked there in my time.
>
> It had the atmosphere of a big family. No one was more important than any one else. We were all of equal value. The prayer life of the Sisters encircled us all. I remember Sister Carmella Bermingham coming to the Pharmacy one day and presenting me with a copy of the 'Daily Office' which she suggested I could say in my spare moments. It was one of my NOT so good days which the older staff will remember was quite often. I reminded Sister

Carmella that I said the litany every day but it was not the Litany of the Saints. This is just an example of the close and relaxed atmosphere between the Sisters and the lay staff. We laughed, cried and fought together. This spirit of the Hospice was mystical.

Another stalwart of the staff, Eileen Purcell, has given a vivid and realistic picture of life in the Wards of Our Lady's Hospice in the 1950s and later.

I started work in the Hospice in 1950. I worked there for many years and I did enjoy the work and was very happy there. I found the nuns, the Sisters of Charity, very just and fair but very strict. They had to be as money was very scarce and the poverty was bad. The Sisters worked very hard all day with little time off just for meals and prayers. We worked under their supervision.

The work was very hard with no modern conveniences. No central heating, so real fires had to be lit in each ward and hot water bottles had to be filled three times a day. They were earthen-ware bottles. There were no disposable sheets or dressings. Sheets had to be washed in a big sink before going to the laundry. Dressings had to be made with cotton wool and gauze. There was no way of sterilising sputum mugs or urinals or bed pans, only to fill a big aluminium bath with boiling water and washing soda.

The beds the patients slept in had hair mattresses and they had to be carbolised twice a week to keep away fleas. The Hospice was kept very clean and it was very pleasant to work in. There was always music, playing, dancing and singing on the wards. Nobody got Christmas off. That was the patients' day. We had good food as the Sisters were self-supporting and we got plenty to eat.

Another illuminating letter is from a retired lady who came to Our Lady's Hospice in the 1960s and 'loved every day'. Her aunt had died in Our Lady's Hospice and her ambition was to be a nurse, but she was not allowed by her family to go to England and the fees for nursing in Ireland were too high. Remembering that the nun in charge of her aunt's ward had told her to 'call up and see her any time she was in the vicinity' she did so one year later and was employed as a nurse assistant. Most nurses 'lived in' at that time except for a few staff nurses. She continues:

> My jobs were heavy. I washed and powdered the rubber sheets, took the temperatures and looked after the linen. We had to have our uniforms spotless as well as our hats and white shoes—a uniform I much prefer to the present day ones. . . . Nurses have more free time now—we had one day off a week and every second Sunday from 2 pm.

Now retired, Anne Gardner lives in St Michael's in the Hospice where she says she 'is treated like a Queen'.

10 Changing diseases, new projects

Because of the increased life span from better housing and diet, the arrival of new drugs and the benefits of surgery and physiotherapy in the crippling joint diseases, Our Lady's Hospice after the Second World War was no longer simply a place to which people were sent to die. Extended Care, then the Rheumatology Unit (1961) and finally the new Palliative Care Unit (1978) became the three divisions of the Hospice. However, in bed numbers, if not in bed turnover, the long-stay patients were always in the majority. Our Lady's Hospice for the Dying became Our Lady's Hospice. The change in name took place in 1964: ignoring the niceties of nomenclature, Dubliners continue to call it 'The Hospice' or 'Harold's Cross'.

All these changes took place on the original site; Our Lady's Hospice is now one of the very few Dublin hospitals still where it was founded. The grounds were always extensive and the new units have replaced in part the dairy farm, orchard and gardens. But much open space has survived the new buildings and their inevitable car parks. Since the purchase of Greenmount in 1845 the only recorded addition to the site was some 60 years later when 'thirteen acres for additional pasturage' were acquired for £1,500. This is the area at the back of the Rheumatology and Palliative Care Units. Then as now there are tree-lined walks for the patients and open stretches of well-mown grass where cows and cattle once grazed.

During and after the Second World War Patrick T. O'Farrell was Visiting Physician to the Hospice. Working with his colleague, in alternate months he paid a daily visit to the wards or visited pa-

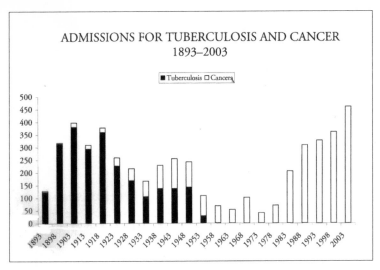

ADMISSIONS FOR TUBERCULOSIS AND CANCER
1893–2003

■ Tuberculosis □ Cancers

tients' homes to decide on the necessity for admission—a practice unchanged since Our Lady's Hospice was founded.

In 1945 he wrote:

> Many prospective patients live in squalor, poverty and sometimes neglect. Internal cancer, pulmonary tuberculosis, advanced heart disease and the ravages of old age form the majority [of the diseases demanding admission]. Many of them are bedridden, some have bed sores and others are completely helpless.[17]

These words paint a vivid picture. The same words could have been used to describe the conditions of the patients since the Hospice opened. What strikes a medical outsider is that good nursing care remained the chief service that the Hospice still provided 80 years after its foundation. Even had a battery of laboratory tests, a plethora of diagnoses, a full pharmacy of medication been available then they would have been less important. Major advances in therapy of all kinds remained in the future. Such advances in the Hospice will be described now.

Between 1898 and 1958 admissions fell from 367 to 206 patients per annum (see page 35). Up to 1945 the average stay ranged from 80 to 120 days and as late as 1953 patients in the Hospice for one week or less reached 40 per cent of the admissions—the great majority of these died. By 1986 the length of stay in Extended Care had increased to an average of 335 days for men and 494 for women. Three-quarters of these patients were now over 75 years of age. Forty years earlier half the patients were under 35 years of age—the young people who died from tuberculosis.

These very different sets of statistics were of course determined by the changing reasons for admission to Our Lady's Hospice: the number of tuberculous patients had been on the wane since the dawn of the twentieth century; tuberculosis was overtaken by cancer as an admission diagnosis in 1953 and soon disappeared; above all people were living longer and their diseases lasted longer because of newer remedies. To look after them a physician with a special interest in geriatrics was needed. In 1962 such a person was appointed: Dr John Fleetwood, who remained working in the Hospice for 30 years. Very soon after his appointment, Fleetwood gave a television talk on 'The Changing Face of Ireland' in which he gave some of the Hospice statistics mentioned above and commented on 'the changing faces in the wards because the beds were immediately requisitioned for others'. He spoke of the arrival of new drugs—outstandingly the antibiotics—which cured many infections, especially tuberculosis which had once inundated the Hospice with moribund patients.

After 33 years fruitful service in Extended Care, much of it working in collaboration with Dr Patrick O'Callaghan, John Fleetwood was succeeded as Medical Director in 1995 by Denis Donohoe who gives an interesting list of the diagnoses of 108 patients in the unit: Alzheimer's Disease—34 patients; cerebro-vascular accidents—22; and Parkinson's Disease—19 patients; were the commonest conditions encountered. The increasing number of patients with motor neurone disease (AMLS, MS, etc.) gets particular mention over the next few years. In 1998 Dr Donohoe was appointed Special Lecturer in Medicine (UCD); the students attend for lectures in Extended Care on Fridays. Of special importance in a long-stay unit is the cooperation with the three major disciplines of occupational therapy, physiotherapy and social work, something encouraged by monthly joint conferences.

Due in part to increased longevity the number of people with chronic joint disease had grown. To look after them a Rheumatologist was needed. He was Dr Jack Molony, who has given the credit[18] for his appointment to Sister Teresa Anthony Heskin, and a joint appointment was made between Our Lady's Hospice and St Vincent's Hospital in Dublin.

The new Rheumatology Unit had 68 beds, including for a while sixteen private rooms. It is a red-bricked, three-storey building designed by J. W. Griffith and Partners and built by W. and J. Bolger. Ever since visitors or patients who lose their way around the Hospice grounds are directed to 'the red building with the statue above the door'. The cost of St Joseph's was £150,000, of which a mere one-fifth came from public funds. John Charles McQuaid, Dublin's Archbishop, formally opened the building on 18 July 1962. At first there were also some long-stay patients in St Joseph's as well as beds for oncology—these last returned to the main building. A few years later St Joseph's acquired a new staircase, a kitchenette, more bathrooms and toilets and a bay-windowed sun room on the first floor. As just described, there were for a time in St Joseph's beds for oncology, i.e. the medical treatment of cancer, especially chemotherapy. This had started in 1964 with the appointment of Dr Jim Fennelly; there were some fourteen beds in St Paul's Ward in the main building. With the opening of an oncology unit in St Vincent's Hospital in 1970 Jim Fennelly transferred his work to that place and oncology largely ceased in the Hospice.

Mention is made above of joint appointments between the Hospice and teaching hospitals. It is convenient to follow up that subject here up to the end of the twentieth century. For rheumatology in St Joseph's let me quote its founding father, Dr Molony:

At the time it [St Joseph's] consisted of approximately 55 beds. Sister Mary de Montfort Maguire was appointed Matron. We both worked together closely over the next 30 years and had some interesting tussles in the early years but formed a very successful partnership. They were very happy years and I can honestly say that I enjoyed my time spent at St Joseph's. We developed an excellent team including doctors from St Vincent's Hospital, nursing staff, physiotherapists, occupational therapists, social workers and secretarial staff. The Unit admitted patients for assessment and rehabilitation from St Vincent's Hospital and general practitioners. Most of these patients suffered from rheumatological and neurological diseases. Weekly staff meetings were held where these programmes were assessed and modified accordingly. Emphasis was on the total patient care concept and each member of the team was conscious of it. The Unit gradually developed into an active Rheumatology and Rehabilitation Centre, the envy of most of our colleagues. It is a unique unit and the only one of its kind in the country. Close liaison was developed with the orthopaedic service at St Vincent's Hospital and monthly conferences were held in the Unit where problem patients were discussed by all members of staff. Orthopaedic surgeons from St Vincent's Hospital attend this conference. St Joseph's works closely with St Anthony's Outpatient Rehabilitation Centre and the Rheumatology Department at St Vincent's Hospital. A new Hydrotherapy Department has now been developed. Professor Barry Bresnihan and Dr Oliver FitzGerald were the other Consultants and have added a great deal to the Unit. They have developed an up-to-date Research Unit which has an international reputation.[18]

Sister de Montfort remained in charge in St Joseph's until her retirement in 1992. She died in 2000.

Much of what the first Director of Rheumatology wrote has been corroborated by his successor Barry Bresnihan who makes three points after 25 years' service in OLH.[19] First, letting light into St Joseph's': the interior was rebuilt in 1978 and the layout became 'brighter and less cramped'. Second, collaboration and cooperation with other disciplines are regarded still as vital factors. Third, the research work continues in cooperation now with Professor Cliodna O'Farrelly of St Vincent's University Hospital; tissue culture in rheumatoid arthritis is the main research activity and has resulted in many international publications.

The practice noted above of doctors working in Our Lady's Hospice before an appointment to St Vincent's Hospital was not a new one—O'Farrell had done this during the Second World War. After the war a future cardiologist to St Vincent's Hospital also worked in Our Lady's Hospice: he was Risteárd Mulcahy, who has written about his spell in Harold's Cross: 'The spectre of increasing and intolerable pain and a distressful end . . . was seldom or never encountered by me.'[20]

When one remembers that the reason Our Lady's Hospice was founded was because St Vincent's Hospital on Stephen's Green could not admit patients dying from infectious diseases and that the two places share a common ethos and ownership the connection is understandable. What has changed are the referrals from hospital to hospice: the traffic is reversed. Those now in Our Lady's Hospice with surgical problems or in need of chemotherapy travel the couple of miles to the general hospital now in Elm Park in Dublin. The practice in rheumatology in this regard has been mentioned already. In fact the traffic has not just reversed, it has become two way. The complexity of modern medicine, with its increasing number of different specialities and the contraction of their focus—all these factors now govern inter-hospital practice, in particular that between a hospice for long-stay patients and an acute general hospital.

Some final comparisons about the changes in length of stay and mortality are necessary when writing about an institution once called 'Our Lady's Hospice for the Dying'. In its early days the Sisters listed with some pride the annual number of deaths—pride because the dying had been given physical and spiritual comfort. Such pride in mortality figures would be anathema today when every disease must have a cure and when faith in life after death is disappearing. As already noted, the proportion of cancer patients in Our Lady's Hospice has changed little over the past half-century, although such sufferers now occupy their own Palliative Care Unit. The rheumatology patients in St Joseph's stay there for an average now of 18 days and the mortality figure is zero. (For details see page 63.)

It is not surprising that the average stay in the long-stay unit there has much increased; for example in 1987 it varied between 183 and 459 days (6–15 months), whereas for the half-century before 1945 it was only 80–120 days. The obvious conclusion follows: lengthy stay means fewer deaths and the reasons for this change over more than a century of Our Lady's Hospice's existence again are clear: different and longer-lasting diseases, improved social conditions, and better and more available medical treatment. There has been another change highlighted by Denis Donohoe: the increase in requests by patients or their relatives for more or different treatments and sometimes in terminal patients for the cessation of all treatment. The public is better informed.

Staff conferences are a form of mutual self-education involving disciplines other than those of the hosting doctors. As in Extended Care and Rheumatology they were to become a twice-weekly feature of the Palliative Care Unit. Junior staff benefit from the discussions of their seniors and enjoy disagreeing with them. In 1999 medical students arrived to attend lectures and ward rounds in all three units. For some of these it is their first exposure to the *raison d'être* of their professional existence: the patient. These undergraduates come from two of Dublin's three medical schools, University College Dublin and Trinity College Dublin. The first joint tutor was Dr Maeve O'Reilly; the present incumbent is Dr Marie Twomey.

The result of these events is that the Hospice is now a recognised teaching hospital, which carries a certain cachet in itself. But apart from education, patients benefit. Active young brains stimulate those they meet, including their teachers. Some patients enjoy the attention of being singled out to discuss their complaints. Involvement in medical research may give an opportunity for altruism. Informed consent by the patient is, of course, mandatory in such cases and there is an Ethics Committee to screen and approve any new clinical trials.

11 Palliative Care, Home Care, Bereavement Support and Bás Solais

The origin of hospices has been described earlier. It was in a London hospice that modern palliative care was born in the 1950s. The phrase 'the hospice movement' is now often used synonymously with palliative care, meaning the treatment of all of a terminal patient's complaints—physical, mental and spiritual, in the knowledge that a medical cure is not possible. As has been written: 'The length of the dying process and the differing appreciation by the patient of its inevitability demand different responses and a larger team of carers.'

The credit for starting this new regime of palliative care is rightly given to Cicely Saunders. She acknowledged her debt to the Irish Sisters of Charity in whose hospice in London, St Joseph's, Hackney, she began her career. Saunders had been a social worker and had nursing experience as a volunteer in London's St Luke's Hospital, as well as St Joseph's—both took terminal cases. Inspired by a personal experience with a patient, she wanted to do more. She qualified in medicine and renewed her visits to St Joseph's, of which she writes:

> The infinitely caring nuns welcomed a doctor who introduced drug sheets and patients' notes and took the time to listen. Instead of 'earning' their morphine by suffering pain first, the patients were offered relief on a regular basis. . . . Patients were freed from the cycle in which their experiences alternated between 'pain-full' to 'pain-free' as one of the nuns recalls it.[22]

Ideas about the relief of pain die hard: that women in labour should not be given analgesics was commonplace practice in mid-twentieth-century Dublin. The dangers of prescribing morphine were well known to patients and carers alike; nevertheless Saunders' insistence that pain relief should be continuous is her lasting achievement. Indeed this change in therapy thinking has spread now to general practice.

Elizabeth Kübler-Ross, like Saunders well known as a writer of quality and a dynamic lecturer, was another standard-bearer in the field of palliative care. Her work started in the USA. Soon, on both sides of the Atlantic, new journals for the new speciality were born. New books were published, newspapers and magazines flowed with this tide of ideas. *On Death and Dying* (1970) was the title of Kübler-Ross's book. Saunders' earlier book *Care of the Dying* (1959) had set the gold standard. The philosophers of ancient Greece were invoked. Theologians joined agnostics in controversy about euthanasia; these debates are ongoing and it is certain that they will continue.

The genesis of the idea for a palliative care unit in Our Lady's Hospice cannot be credited to just one of the Sisters or doctors. As with the foundation of the Hospice a century earlier, it was a response to an urgent need—not just the age-old problem of nursing those dying from any cause but the more particular problem of those with a fatal form of cancer nearing its inevitable end; the phrase used at the time in Our Lady's Hospice was 'acute terminally ill patients'.

It was fitting that this new venture of palliative care became established in the centenary year of the opening of the Hospice in 1879. To celebrate the centenary Sister Katherine Butler wrote an interesting account of Our Lady's Hospice called *We Help Them Home*. The other happy coincidence is that the Order's Superior General, Sister Francis Rose O'Flynn, and the Rectress and Matron of the Hospice at the time of the centenary, Sister Ignatius Phelan, should both be based there today and remain involved and active. Their years of service at high command level are listed among their colleagues in religion in Appendix 3.

The thinking behind palliative care, the ideals and ethos of this form of treatment are very well put by Jack McCarthy, the first medical director of the new unit:

Recent years have seen the birth of the modern concept of Hospice care. This really means intensive care of the dying. Death is a natural process and like birth requires skilled medical and nursing care.

There comes a time in all illness when treatment aimed at cure is useless and annoying. It is important to recognise this and direct treatment towards the control of disturbing symptoms. To say that nothing more can be done is wrong. Indeed at no time is total care of the patient and his family more important.

The patient's insight into his illness should be considered very early and when the physician feels the time is right, the most optimistic version of his disease which is usually cancer should be given to the patient. This is a most important and delicate matter and requires all the skill and experience of the doctor. No information should be forced on those who make it obvious they do not want it. Lies should always be avoided. Telling the family and not the patient leads to a further tissue of lies which demands more lies as the disease progresses. The patient who probably knows all along, will now lose confidence in doctor and relatives and probably withdraw inwards at a time when open communication is all important.

Pain is feared by most patients and relatives and many cancer patients expect a painful death. Nothing is further from the truth. All pain can be prevented by careful medical care. So-called intractable pain is pain which is somewhat more difficult to control. On admission the patient is told there will be no pain and this promise is kept.

Hospice staff are above all caring staff and aware that they are privileged to be admitted to enter the family circle of the very ill patient at such an important time. They are chosen for their professional skill which should be of the highest standard.

The modern Hospice is a cheerful place and the atmosphere of tranquillity will often lead to a reduction in the pain threshold and consequently a reduction in medication.[23]

There is nothing unusual about the proportions of the different types of cancer[24, 25] in patients admitted to palliative care in Our

Lady's Hospice in the 1980s. Topping the list in 1986 for women is cancer of the breast, for men it is lung cancer—these leading sites are the same as the national incidence. More important and interesting is the length of stay of the patients: the average was 30 days. The next year shows no change in the figures for tumour site and stay. Ten years later 26 days was the average stay and by the year 2000 it was down to 24 days. Throughout this decade the total number of annual admissions usually topped 400. Fifty years earlier in very different circumstances the average stay before death of the cancer patients in Our Lady's Hospice was 66 days.

In part the fall in the average stay in the unit can be attributed to the work of the Home Care and Day Care teams: more accurate assessment of the urgency for admission, more use of respite care, better liaison with both the family doctor and the patient's own family. Evidence for this is the increase in discharges from 20 per cent to 27 per cent in one year. As in the Extended Care Unit, women on average spent longer in palliative care—up to a week more in 1986. The overall mortality rate in the Palliative Care Unit is naturally high: 74 per cent in 2000.

Surprising to some is the fact that discharges do take place from a unit for the terminally ill. Respite care means not just patient care but relief, respite for family and friends from the 24-hour task of caring for those near death or for those bed-bound by lingering motor neurone disease. Weekends at home are a boost for those able to make the journey in the confidence that on Monday morning their hospice bed and another warm welcome await them. In one of the years mentioned above such 'discharges' made up a quarter of all the admissions. The final point is that some patients or their families prefer to die in their own home and may leave the Hospice as a 'discharge' for this reason.

Most of what follows I owe to Sister Ignatius Phelan. In a lengthy interview[26] she gave a vivid and fact-filled view of the happenings and the personalities responsible for the inception of palliative care. In 1974 Sister Ignatius came to Harold's Cross from St Vincent's

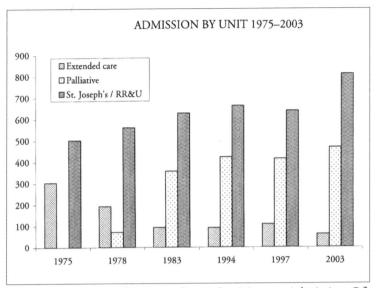

ADMISSION BY UNIT 1975–2003

- ▨ Extended care
- ▢ Palliative
- ▨ St. Joseph's / RR&U

Hospital. Her new role meant three jobs: Matron, Admission Officer and Superior of the local Community. The Rheumatology Unit and that for Extended Care comprised the Hospice's work up to this time. The queue waiting for beds was as long as O'Connell Street. The medical staff consisted of three doctors—Fleetwood, O'Callaghan and Molony. There were but two junior doctors, neither resident. The patients in Extended Care were elderly, static, but usually fulfilled in their captive role of old age. Younger people needing nursing care could not be admitted to share wards with such geriatric cases. Sister Ignatius had been a theatre sister, a post committed to action; after some time running the Hospice the need for action in a different field became clear to her.

Encouraged by the Superior General, Sister Francis Rose O'Flynn, Sister Ignatius crossed the Irish Sea to St Joseph's Hospice in London. Six weeks were spent there and also in St Christopher's, then ten years old and still run by its foundress Cicely Saunders. Already the Sisters in Hackney had commenced home visiting of the seriously ill. Palliative care in its modern sense was in full flow. Had Dublin lagged behind?

The new ideas led to new hopes and plans by the Sisters in

Harold's Cross. But the 70s of the twentieth century were times of recession. Money was scarce. The Department of Health was slow to fund a new enterprise which called for the expenditure of at least £70,000. Charles Haughey was Minister for Health. In his Department worked a doctor, Niall Tierney, to whom Sister Ignatius has given the credit for nudging the wheels of the civil service. A grant from the Department of Health of £25,000 resulted. A second, much-needed grant soon followed—this time the credit is given to the prayers of the Sisters while on Retreat. The Congregation supplied the balance. The new and specialised unit needed professional direction. The post was advertised. From the applicants five doctors were interviewed. The one chosen was a young Englishman with experience of palliative care in London. After many months of uncertainty he did not take up the appointment.

The runner-up of those interviewed and ultimately the first holder of the Hospice appointment was Dr John McCarthy, a man from Lixnaw in Co. Kerry generally called Jack. He was in practice in Co. Limerick and also Medical Officer to the sanatorium in Foynes. Earlier he had worked in Peamount Sanatorium where he was first involved with the care of the dying. 'He was a good listener, he had the manner and he had love.'[27] Countless patients now dead, countless relatives have borne witness to the truth of these comments about Jack McCarthy. Chance may have decided his appointment but his success remains unquestioned. One facet of Jack McCarthy's work well remembered to this day is how he used to start his morning in Our Lady's Hospice. Maura McDonnell, who worked closely with him in Palliative Care, has described his routine. He took his station every morning at 7.30 am at the window on the left side of the main door of the Hospice:

> He was there to listen, to deal with any problem and most of all to offer his support. . . . After a long night on duty the welcome sound of his footstep was a great comfort . . . His special way with people: who they were, where they came from, how they felt and what and who mattered to them— all these facets made patients feel safe and secure.[27]

Not only the patients in palliative care were grateful to Jack McCarthy: staff of all kinds came to him with their problems.

This first Palliative Care Unit was formally opened in June of 1978. The cost of remodelling the two wards, St Anne's and St Charles, came to £116,000—the increase in the budget was more than half the original estimate. The Department grants and the subvention by the Congregation left a sizeable balance unpaid but this was cleared immediately by a then anonymous benefactor, Francis Morrin, son of the Vincent's surgeon Frank Morrin. A new era of palliative care had started in Harold's Cross—it was the first such unit in this country. Bed numbers in the two wards totalled 34.

Any person with terminal cancer nowadays should be free of physical pain. Freedom from worry and from fear may be more difficult to achieve—peace of mind, peace of body and soul are goals not so readily attained. The process is a gradual one but sometimes reaching this goal happens suddenly as the following account demonstrates.

Twenty years ago a middle-aged widow from Dublin's Liberties died from cancer of the breast in Our Lady's Hospice. Her only son John developed a brain tumour three years later, when he was eighteen years of age. Following radiotherapy he came to the Hospice as his mother had, but he was very unhappy and unsettled—he had hoped that surgery would help him but this was not a viable option. One day some of his young friends called as usual to see him and gave their news of a concert they were going to the next day: the group Abba performing in the Gaiety Theatre. Would or could John join them? But it was the last night of the tour and tickets were unobtainable, the idea was impossible. Hearing this problem Sister Ignatius got busy on the phone and finally persuaded the Gaiety Manager to allow the dying boy to attend the concert—responsibility was taken by Our Lady's Hospice. Late that night a transformed patient returned to the Hospice saying that he had had 'a whale of a time'. Next morning he confirmed his mind-change: 'I lived for the first time since my mother died. For the first time I accepted both her death and my cancer.' This peace of mind continued for the two weeks of life left to him: terminal care has many faces.

The demand for palliative care was so great that a new unit was needed and intensive fundraising began. In 1987 international fame came to a Dublin southsider when Stephen Roche won the Tour de France, that pinnacle of bicycle road racing. He gave his bike to Our Lady's Hospice; at auction it went for £28,000. The bike was then returned by the bidder. By an interesting coincidence in that same year of 1987 Stephen Roche made another link with Our Lady's Hospice: as one of those nominated as 'People of the Year' he was joined for this prestigious national honour by Sister Francis Rose O'Flynn and Sister Ignatius Phelan. In a book dominated by Dublin and Dubliners it is justice to record that these two ladies come from Derry and Clonmel. These same Sisters were the driving force behind the building of the new Education Centre, the ward overhead, St Patrick's and the new Palliative Care Centre. The Minister for Health, Barry Desmond provided £250,000 over three years. An elite team of the gracious and the good from the Irish Hospice Foundation excelled in fundraising. The Sisters of Charity provided a large contribution and ultimately the building costs of £3.85 million for the Palliative Centre were reached. Building of a new Palliative Care Unit began in 1991. The result was a 'splendid red-brick red-roofed low slung building' designed by J. W. Griffith and Partners. The work of builders John Sisk later won a Construction Excellence Award. In June of 1993 this custom-built Palliative Care Unit, appropriately called Caritas, was officially opened by the President of Ireland Mary Robinson after a blessing by Desmond Connell the diocesan Archbishop.

An important element of the new unit was the provision of overnight accommodation for the relatives of those near death. Sometimes this means an extra bed in a single room, sometimes another bed in the patient's room. Like so many other 'new' developments in Our Lady's Hospice this was but a revival of a practice which had started in the 1880s. The flexibility of visiting hours then and now is also something important and there are enough comfortable chairs and quiet spots for those who want to sit and wait.

The thinking behind patient management will vary with the personality of the carers and their particular role in the team responsible for palliative care. Michael Kearney, the second Medical Director of Palliative Care, developed the ethos of the unit to include the idea of palliative healing. This meant the revival of the distinction made by the medical thinkers of classical times.

Hippocrates believed in treating the patients' symptoms with the armamentarium of his times: potions, pills, poultices and unguents. Knowledge of the true nature of most diseases was then unknown but if the cause of the illness could not be treated, pain, anxiety and other symptoms might be relieved: this became the Hippocratic approach, still practised in principle more than two millennia later. However, his fellow Greek Asclepiades favoured co-operation by doctors with the patient's autonomous (self originating) dynamism; this involved inclusive psychology—the thinking and reactions of the patient to their own physical problems. Fittingly Asclepiades has been described as a physician 'learned in philosophy'.[28]

This double approach to the person with cancer is ongoing in the Palliative Care Unit. At the weekly case conferences the attendance includes doctors of all grades of experience, the senior nurse in charge, the Hospice chaplain, a social worker, a physiotherapist and an occupational therapist. Sometimes there will be an interested visitor from a similar profession. A psychiatrist may be consulted in some cases. The meetings with members of the family following discussion with the patient play a vital part in care. Before and after admission to the unit the Home Care Team is deeply involved. Apart from the usual bath or shower, nurse-assisted or not, the hydrotherapy pool is available, again with trained help. Asclepiades would approve—he emphasised bathing, diet and exercise. There is a wide choice of dishes from the menu brought round by a volunteer; sensibly there is no insistence on low fat diets or butter substitutes. A major difference from the usual hospital regime is the flexibility of mealtimes for the sicker patients: no dawn calls to breakfast, the possibility of night-time tea and toast. Anybody nearing their end and used to taking an alcoholic drink is encouraged to do so and if relatives have not provided the necessary bottle there is a well-stocked trolley which makes the rounds of the wards. 'Bringing the patient out for a pint' is essential therapy for those loyal to draught stout. 'Smoking causes cancer', the warning on cigarette packets loses its relevance in a terminal care unit: a smoking room for patients and their anxious visitors caters for this need.

Clearly the amount of exercise possible, necessary or wanted by any patient varies greatly. For some the help of the physiotherapist is a great boon. For others the answer may be aromatherapy—one lady from Galway cheerfully acknowledged that 'it had become an addiction'. For the patient to be able to wash and dress means the retention of dignity and independence; when these routines become impossible there follows the sometimes difficult stage of dependency on others. Gracious acceptance of this marks another milestone on the road to peace.

In 1992 another progressive step was taken: the admission of HIV patients to single rooms in the unit. In cooperation with Dr Fiona Mulcahy of St James's Hospital such people—often young, some with cancer—came to Our Lady's Hospice for respite or terminal care. Their numbers are small and a few of them have tuberculosis—a reminder of early admissions to Our Lady's Hospice.

Home Care

In 1985 the palliative care service was developed by the establishment of Home Care in which patients could receive almost all the benefits of palliative care in the psychological and physical comfort of their own homes.

*The Home Care team arranging the visits for the day (1986): (l–r)
Sr J. Ignatius, Nurses Kathleen Maher, Kathy Redmond, Dr Veronie
Hanley, Noreen Holland*

> Home care is the perfect alternative to in-Hospice care where the patient
> wishes to remain at home and the family members are able to cope. . . . A
> Home Care team comprising medical and nursing staff working in co-opera-
> tion with general practitioners, hospitals and public health nurses can bring
> the highest standard of care offered by the Hospice into the homes of so
> many patients where the above criteria are met.

Thus wrote Sister Ignatius Phelan[29] who piloted the service from
the start. The new Home Care enterprise needed funds and the
Irish Cancer Society filled the breach in 1985 with a grant over three
years. The Patron of that Society was a gentleman from Poland who
lived in Celbridge, Co. Kildare, Vincent Kozziel, and his interest in
Our Lady's Hospice went further than his role in the Cancer Society. Sisters Paula Gleeson and Ignatius Phelan attended a Palliative/
Home Care meeting in Montreal, Canada. When work was finished their entertainment was taken care of by this Polish man: he
took his Irish friends to a nightclub.

But staff also were needed; this time the funding came from the
Department of Health which agreed to the request for a staff of

twelve medical, nursing and secretarial personnel for the home visiting venture. Equally important was liaison with the local family doctors who were consulted at a meeting held in Mount Carmel Hospital. By mutual agreement it was decided that the request for home care must come from the patient's own family doctor. Nearly twenty years on this vital link in the chain of care continues unbroken and it is routine to report regularly to the doctors about their patient's condition and to get and make suggestions about the future. In 2000 the Medical Director Michael Kearney reported over 500 patients in one year seen by Home Care and 235 deaths at home.[30]

Bereavement support

Started at much the same time as Home Care was that other backup to the Palliative Care Unit, the Bereavement Support Service. This was at the initiative of Mary Redmond, the Chairperson of the Hospice Foundation and the late Thérèse Brady of the Department of Psychology, University College Dublin. Sister Francis Rose and Hospice staff were happy to co-operate. Credit is also given to John Murphy SJ, who earlier had started the Bethany Support Group in Tabor House, Dublin.[31]

October 1986 saw the first training programme for eight volunteers. In the following year invitations went out to the relatives or friends of people who had died in the Hospice eight weeks earlier. Monthly meetings followed. Attending these were the Hospice chaplains, staff and volunteers. At the first five meetings there were 80 people in all. Most of the bereaved came but once, others up to four times; all of them greatly appreciated the service. The need to unburden themselves and to share their loss was very apparent. A follow-up by phone call confirmed the value of the service. Ten years later the service had expanded greatly; volunteers numbered 30 and now spent a year in training; the sessions with the bereaved increased to three times a month and were attended, not just by those whose relatives had died in the Palliative Care Unit, but from Extended Care as well. Total attendances in 1996 numbered 910.

The routine established then continues now little changed. Three months after the death of any patient in any unit letters are sent to the nearest relatives of the deceased inviting them to attend a meeting in Our Lady's Hospice. These are held on three Mondays in each month either in the evening or after lunch. Attendance numbers of the bereaved are variable but 20 or so volunteers are always present: these are allocated randomly to anyone seeking further help. The sessions are no longer chaired by Dr Thérèse Brady: sadly she died in January 1999. Dr Mary Redmond, who had asked Thérèse to set up the Bereavement Service in 1985 has written: '. . . the Service has grown, has reached so many people, so many hospice groups . . . has maintained the highest professional standards. Therese is and has been at the centre of the Service.' After her death Sister Francis Rose O'Flynn also paid tribute: 'Thérèse was a lady who combined a high level of professionalism with a human and friendly touch.'

In charge of the Bereavement Support Service now is Dr Susan Delaney of the Irish Hospice Foundation, a worthy successor to the first to hold this post: she, like all those whom she helped, is remembered at the Annual Bereavement Mass each December: a reunion in prayer that coincides appropriately with 'Light up a Life', an event to be described in a later section.

Bás Solais 2000: Death with Illumination

The Bás Solais meeting was Ireland's first International Palliative Care Conference; it was held in Dublin Castle from 7 to 9 June 2000. It was a joint venture between Our Lady's Hospice and the Irish Cancer Society and was attended by 500 delegates from 26 countries. In all there were 72 presentations and the proceedings were reported at length in the daily newspapers; later many were published in the professional journals. The organising committee for the conference was chaired by Dr Liam O'Siorain who had begun work in the Palliative Care Unit of Our Lady's Hospice in 1995.

The next year he succeeded Michael Kearney as Medical Director, the third holder in an outstanding line in this important post.

The official opening of the conference took place on the afternoon of the first day, 7 June and was performed by the President of Ireland Mary McAleese who then talked with the organisers and delegates. The Minister for Health and Children Micheál Martin also addressed the meeting and made clear the deep interest of his Department in hospice care and its future development. In the morning of that same day the *de facto* beginning of Bás Solais had taken place with inaugural addresses by Liam O'Siorain and Sister Una O'Neill. Sister Una was then and still is the Superior General of the Sisters of Charity; she spoke of our attitudes to death and about the idea of 'embracing death'; her thoughts are discussed in a later section of this book. The first plenary session began with a talk on 'Lessons in Living from the Dying' by Dame Cicely Saunders, the doyenne of modern palliative care. In answer to a question about the worries of some patients about having unfinished business Saunders replied, 'I have never met a terminal cancer patient who said they should have spent more time in the office.'[32]

One of the most impressive talks was that by a patient from St Gabriel's Ward in Our Lady's Hospice. Bob Collins gave a moving account of his struggle with cancer despite the very short notice that he got before addressing hundreds of international delegates.

An unusual feature of the meeting was the Robert Pope Exhibition sponsored by the Foundation of that name. This artistic element of the exhibition was the work of this young cancer patient and described as 'a powerful visual representation of one person's journey and his struggles with life in the face of cancer treatment'.[33] His parents Mr and Mrs William Pope were responsible for mounting their son's work in Dublin Castle.

12 Other disciplines

Only for the last decade have there been published Annual Reports for Our Lady's Hospice, although there were two such reports in the 1880s. For the preceding century the Annals of the Sisters are the sole primary source for any historical account.

The *Annual Report* for 2000 is 40 pages long with many photographs to illuminate the printed word. There are as many as 25 separate reports from the various departments. Comment on all of these is not my brief—the number-jungle of accountancy, the mysteries of catering, the philosophy of human resources are beyond my ken. However, brief comments on a few of the departments having direct patient contact are called for—this is the so-called 'paramedical' area. Just as important is something never mentioned in any report: one long-stay, chair-bound man called David enjoyed sitting outside and has put it well: 'Nobody [working in the Hospice] ever passes me without a cheerful world. Often they stop for a chat.' Plainly a spirit of caring is not confined to nurses and doctors.

One theme common to most of the departmental reports is education which is mentioned in all of the medical and nursing areas and also for the Departments of Physiotherapy, Social Work and Occupational Therapy which are dealt with below. For some years there has been a separate Education Department, headed at the time of writing by Nurse Tutor Marianne McGiffin; previously education was co-ordinated by Philip Larkin. The Department of Social Work reports conferences, workshops and student placements. But continuing education of staff is not a new venture: in 1987 the Education Unit opened with a six-week course on 'The Continuing Care of the Dying Patient and Family'. The Tutor then was Anne Hayes who became Co-ordinator of Complementary and Supportive Therapies: aromatherapy/massage, touch therapy, art and music therapies. During the year 2000 nearly 300 patients attended sessions such as those listed.

The group of Hospice helpers known as Volunteers are not of course the only people working without tangible reward in Our Lady's Hospice. At the apex of control is the Board of Management which has six committees. These are Executive, Health and Safety, Research, Finance, Education and Mission. It is interesting how recent is the founding of this governing body: 1994. In 2000 it had fourteen members and was chaired by Sister Francis Rose O'Flynn. It was decided that the Board should always include a nominated medical person who, if absent asked another member of the medical staff to attend.

Who made the important decisions during the 115 years before the Board began work? Very naturally it was the Sisters of Charity: ownership has both rights and duties, powered in this case by the Order's mission of helping others. The local superior was the Chief Executive Officer and also the Matron, backed up by the Ministress and the Community. Consultation with higher authority meant reference to the Generalate and its Superior. The Dublin Hierarchy was available for advice; it will be remembered what a good friend to the Order was William Walshe the Archbishop at the time of the foundation of the Hospice. Other than this sketchy outline of the command structure details are lacking.

By now it is nothing new in hospitals owned by religious orders that the Chief Executive Officer is a lay person. For brief spells there were two such holders of this office before the arrival in 1973 of a professional administrator—Michael Murphy, happily still in post. His cheerfulness and quiet competence make his role acceptable to all; like many others his job title has changed: from Secretary Manager to Chief Executive Officer.

Suprastructures, infrastructures, committees, conferences and continuing education, all these activities plus day to day management and patient care inevitably mean big staff numbers. It is not valid to compare such numbers now with 50 years ago, the complexity of today's activities did not then exist. What is relevant is the resultant rise in expenditure in salaries—75 per cent of all expenditure in 2000 went towards these. In 1950 beds in Our Lady's Hospice numbered 140 and staff consisted of 100 people, today there are 190 beds staffed by 550 people, some part-time. Where once a single person staffed administration there are now 21. Four new therapy departments and new disciplines such as information technology are now in place. A few jobs no longer exist such as farm workers: the posts of 'herd' and 'poultry maid' are no more. Instead of the resident farm steward and his alsatian dog security officers and their TV cameras patrol the grounds.

Physiotherapy

The first published record to mention physiotherapy in Our Lady's Hospice is in the 1979 book[13] but details are not given. It is certain however that there was physiotherapy in some form from the start of rheumatology in the 1960s. Staff numbers then were few but by 1997 there were nine full-time physiotherapists servicing not just rheumatology but also extended and palliative care patients. This burgeoning of a paramedical discipline is something common to most hospitals but the need for such a service is greater where the patients are older, stay longer and include younger people with joint or motor neurone disease.

Eithne Walsh's report for 1999[33] provides the essential facts about workloads (see Table 12.1). Not surprisingly rheumatology patients head the list. A pool was built and opened in 1997 and hydrotherapy, although catering for all three units in Our Lady's Hospice, again is used mainly by those with arthritis. The number of attendances continues to rise: for example in 2000 they were up by 442 from the previous year to give a total of more than 5,000 attendances by 668 patients.

Table 12.1 Physiotherapy statistics for 1997–9

Unit	Patient numbers			Attendances		
	1997	1998	1999	1997	1998	1999
Rheumatology (St Joseph's)	615	658	715	7,594	8,431	8,418
Extended Care patients	167	100	100	4,902	7,966	6,897
classes	122	92	55	1,001	915	810
Hydrotherapy	n/a	n/a	626	1607	3,842	4,612
Palliative Care	193	147	206	1593	1,194	1,647
Day Care	51	55	58	274	256	223

The increase in staff numbers mentioned earlier was greatest in the early 1990s when numbers almost doubled in two years as Valerie Dagg reported.[35] In common with all other departments in Our Lady's Hospice education flourishes: undergraduate physiotherapy students from both University College Dublin and Trinity College Dublin attend on clinical placement. There are in-house lectures and external courses covering post-graduate needs. Co-operation with colleagues in St Vincent's University Hospital is close, particularly with St Anthony's Rehabilitation Centre; one important facet of this link is to ensure that the advice given to patients is consistent in both centres: it will be remembered that it is to St Vincent's/St Anthony's that the outpatients from Our Lady's Hospice rheumatology go—instructions to them must be the same in both places.

Occupational Therapy

In the past Occupational Therapy (OT) was practised mainly in sanatoria, in psychiatric hospitals or in long-stay orthopaedic hospitals; children as well as adults needed something to occupy their heads and hands. There has been an explosive expansion in this discipline over the last half-century: OT Departments are active now also in institutions for the disabled and geriatric units. Our Lady's Hospice has kept pace.

Table 12.2 Occupational therapy: patient numbers

Unit	1999	2000
Rheumatology Rehabilitation	698	706
Palliative Care		
In-patients	207	252
Day Care	74	85
Extended Care	145	146
Total patients	1,124	1,189

Occupational Therapy in Harold's Cross started in the 1960s. Rheumatology patients were the first to benefit but soon the need for this form of therapy spread to Extended Care and to those with cancer including such patients in day care. But the biggest demand comes from the Rheumatology Unit as is shown in the table above, taken from Deirdre Rowe's report for 2000.

From its beginnings OT was a multidisciplinary concept; the close co-operation with the physiotherapists is understandable and essential. As in Palliative Care, treatment based on the whole patient is the aim—the individual with different abilities and disabilities, different hopes, motivations and willpower. Separate divisions became necessary for palliative, for extended and for day care following the start of OT in rheumatology. The later initiatives took place in the 1990s. 1989 had been a milestone—the start of Activities of Daily Living (ADL) assessments: getting out of bed, using the bathroom, dressing, using the kitchen: all the everyday essentials once taken for granted. The appropriate rooms for relearning these routine tasks were built thanks to a grant from the Arthritis Foundation of Ireland. More work and more staff meant more space and purpose-built rooms. In Extended Care OT moved from a first-floor room opposite St Mary's Ward to a ground-floor unit near St Charles Ward. In the same years covered in the table there were an additional 857 requests for consultation or intervention by the OT team; this number was double that for the preceding year 1999. As with some other departments, statistics are not given in the most recent Annual Reports.

Education

As with other disciplines in Our Lady's Hospice education is ongoing. Field work placements in Our Lady's Hospice for BSc students in Trinity College have been an annual event for some time and from England have come students from the Universities of Oxford and Northumbria. Staff members attend postgraduate programmes towards Masters' degrees. Internal meetings transcend professional boundaries and there is liaison with colleagues in St Vincent's University Hospital and Cappagh Orthopaedic Hospital.

Social Work

The first appointment to this new Department came in 1990; three years later involvement with bereavement counselling began; such counselling is now a separate division in the Social Work Department and is covered in the Palliative Care account. Before the end of the century there had developed involvement by the Department in fifteen separate committees, a phenomenon common to the age. By 1999 there was a total of 604 referrals mostly for family work from the Extended, Palliative, Home and Day Care Units and another 84 referrals for bereavement counselling. Within the department education is ongoing; diplomas in gestalt therapy and palliative care, higher degrees and student placements from University College Dublin. Permanent staff in medical social work now number six plus one temporary social worker/bereavement counsellor.

Volunteers

For some years the idea of establishing a work force of voluntary labour in Our Lady's Hospice had been mooted. The better to use this pool of the charitable minded, the Board appointed a Volunteer Co-Ordinator in 1992. She was Carol Mullan whose brief it was to recruit the volunteers, provide training and control and co-ordinate their work. Within a few months Carol had started something that has become an outstanding success ever since : 'Light up a Life'.

Every year on the Sunday nearest to 9 December—the anniversary of the day when Our Lady's Hospice first opened its doors to the needy—the lights on a pine tree 35-foot high are turned on—a Christmas tree with a difference. The tree stands in front of the main door of Our Lady's Hospice and the illumination is turned on by a notability as important as the President of Ireland. In addition, innumerable small candles cover the ground around the tree. Television cameras turn, press bulbs flash and the crowd fills all the open space. This annual event is more than a public entertainment: it is used for fundraising under the inspired banner of 'Light up a Life' and in 1997 the sum raised was £150,000. Apart from the mechanical job of erecting and illuminating the giant tree, all the other work created by 'Light up a Life' is in the hands of the volunteers. For most of the year there are numerous other activities summarised with hours worked in Table 12.3 made out by Olive Skerrit for the *Annual Report* of 2000. 'Each volunteer slot is 3–4 hours and some volunteers actually do two slots per week.'

As may be seen from this table the roles of volunteers span the spectrum. 'Drivers' are those with cars who collect patients attending day care and bring them home again, or any trip needing transport. In the millennium year of the table the total number of volunteers was 230, doing part-time work that for some seems to be whole-time. The average attendance recorded in the roll book on any weekday in one recent year was 19 people and over Saturday and Sunday it averages 10 volunteers. The 'Year of the Volunteer'—2001—saw a big increase in these figures.

As the first person to be responsible for allotting tasks to this new labour force Carol's job demanded diplomacy and personnel skills, qualities she had in abundance. To this day the memory of her friendly personality brings a smile to the face of any veteran

Table 12.3 Volunteers' workload

Extended Care Unit		
Per day 18–20	Per week 100	400 hours weekly
Palliative Care Unit		
Per day 4	Per week 28	
	plus floaters 12	160 hours weekly
Hospice Shop		
Per day 2	Per week 14	
	plus floaters 6	40 hours weekly
Coffee Shop		
Per day 6	Per week 36	
	plus floaters 10	128 hours weekly
Day Care Unit		
1 hostess	3 volunteers per day	15 hours weekly
1 handcare volunteer	3 volunteers per day	15 hours weekly
General drivers	12	45 hours weekly
Eucharist ministers	10	

volunteer.

In 1996 Carol Mullan became Funding and Resource Co-Ordinator. The success of 'Light up a Life' demanded more time and there were other fundraising activities such as vintage car rallies in 1997 and 1998. Olive Skerritt replaced Carol as Volunteer Co-Ordinator. Carolyn Roe was her Assistant Co-Ordinator, but when Olive retired in 2003 Carolyn took her place in what is now a joint appointment with Walter Walsh. Olive Skerritt's well-earned retirement was a brief one: she died but a few months later. Her work will be remembered.

Apart from talking and above all listening to the patients in the long stay unit, giving them midmorning tea or soup, wheeling them to and from Mass, to Occupational Therapy class, to the hairdresser or outside to the grounds, there are other volunteer activities. Trips in the Hospice minibus range from the National Museum and Gallery to the Botanical Gardens in Glasnevin.

Before Christmas or during the summer sales the bus takes patients to raid the shops and stores—being in a wheelchair does not dampen the ardour for bargain hunting. In the evenings there may be in-house entertainment or concerts by outside groups, events which again mean patient mobilisation by the volunteers. Annually there is an art exhibition held in the Day Care Unit which draws the public as well as patients and staff. For this the artists may keep a token sum and the necessary staffing and selling by a special group of ladies—'volunteers on attachment'.

13 The farm and grounds of Our Lady's Hospice

Mention has been made of the purchase of an additional 13 acres for the farm in 1910. Dairy cows supplied milk to the Hospice for many years but details about the herd are not now known. In 2001 Joe Curtis published a book called *Harold's Cross*, a book bristling with facts and backed by much research about this area of Dublin. Joe had been an altar boy in Our Lady's Hospice from the age of seven but his activities there became far more wide ranging and included 'holiday jobs helping out on the farm for which Mother Francis Joan O'Rourke paid us ten shillings a day, but generally we helped out without payment and would have paid the nuns to be allowed to participate.'[36]

Joe Curtis and his friend Joe Crowe cleaned out hen runs and painted chain-link fences, weeded paths, swept up leaves, helped in the haymaking and picked potatoes, a list which covers some of the activities in Our Lady's Hospice farm. His account describes the years 1965–75. Pig keeping is mentioned; 'hundreds of hens'; turkey chicks for Christmas; a duck pond. In charge of the turkeys for many years was Sister Irene Carroll. When she retired and became chair-bound her passage along the long corridor was a triumphal progress of friendly greetings from all sides. The Christian names of the farm workers are given in Joe's book: Jim —cows; Peter—pigs; Christy—the garden; George—the boiler; Ned—foreman. Most of these men lived where they worked, e.g. George in the gate lodge; as well as being the boilerman he collected the Hospice post from the Rathmines sorting office. The fact that he did this job on a motorbike appealed to schoolboy Joe.

The foreman 'Ned' was Ned Ryan, who was to give sterling service to Our Lady's Hospice for another 30 years: he died after a brief illness in December 2000, still in harness. In the *Annual Report* for that year Michael Murphy wrote of 'the many and varied achievements of Ned's life and his proud service to Our Lady's Hospice.'

In Our Lady's Hospice farming ceased 'about 1990' according to Joe Curtis. What continued and will continue is the care of the gardens: these are now in the highly competent care of Eileen Nolan, John O'Shea and Gary Redmond, all of whom work full-time. Surviving from the early days of the Hospice is that plot known as 'the nuns' garden', now used more often by patients than Sisters; from the long-stay wards come people pushed in their wheelchairs by friends or volunteers. Apart from flower beds, roses, arbours and a summer house, there is a long, heated glasshouse, all of these in immaculate order.

One of the many attractive features of the Palliative Care Unit are the mini-gardens between the wards; shrubs, dwarf trees, rockeries, fountains and floodlighting at night give the bed-bound a changing and restful view. Patio doors from the wards allow sitting out of doors for those still able to enjoy fresh air. The extensive lawns at the back of both Palliative Care and St Joseph's provide a green vista for patients and staff and much mowing for John O'Shea and his team.

The immediate reason for the end of farming in Our Lady's Hospice was the building of the Palliative Care Unit which started in 1991. John O'Shea, mentioned above, worked in the farm from 1979 and has given an account of the activities there in his time.[37] The dairy cows were Friesians, about a dozen in all, along with a few calves and dry stock. Pigs numbered 40 and included a boar. The farm staff consisted of three men with some part-time help.

The diversion underground of the Poddle was the other and related event of 1991. This tributary of the Liffey had run on a line parallel with Harold's Cross Road and alongside the wall separating Our Lady's Hospice from the gardens of the houses on Harold's Cross Road. Upstream and downstream there were once mill ponds and mill races but the pond in Our Lady's Hospice was reserved for ducks: it disappeared in the same year as did the no-longer-needed bridge under the avenue. Flooding by the Poddle became but a memory. The last evidence of farming to disappear was the hay barn which survived beside the back gate until 1993.

Trees are an important part of any garden or grounds. Patients can watch the branches swaying with the changing winds and seasons; any outside distraction is a help to the bed bound. Among the 70 or so trees in Our Lady's Hospice there are as many as 13 different species, the great majority of them broad leaf. Very recently a study of their condition was made.[38] Not surprisingly the construction work of the past 40 years—five new detached buildings along with car parks—caused root damage but not in an extensive way and the maintenance work recommended in the survey is already in progress. The most striking of Our Lady's Hospice's trees are the limes lining the walks on the west side, 30 lime trees, some pollarded. Here too are single examples of birch, alder, liquid amber and walnut. Near the rose garden are horse chestnuts, poplars and a copper beech tree. Happily conifers of the common type are not to be seen: three Monterey cypresses better represent the pine tree family. Devoid of trees is the field to the right of the avenue, a gap that may be filled.

14 Faith in practice

It is time to dip a toe into the deep waters of religion. Despite the validity of the claims of hospices to be nondenominational, different faiths mean different practices. Like the hospices these practices have changed over the last century and a quarter.

Humphreys has studied the effects of a differing ethos in two London hospices, both founded around the turn of the nineteenth century.[39] The first of these, St Luke's Home in Regent's Park in London was affiliated to the Methodist West London Mission. The second, St Joseph's in Hackney, was run by the Sisters of Charity and influenced by the older OLH in Harold's Cross. From the early written records of these two hospices Humphreys concluded that in Hackney 'the Sisters saw the death-bed as the arena in which "the conflict with the enemies of salvation" was undergone. They defined their task as the rescuing of sin-laden souls from the clutches of the Evil One in the last few hours.'

In St Luke's the wording may be Wesleyan but the basic idea of salvation is the same: 'Pain, so hard sometimes to understand, has made our patients realise, as nothing else would, that they must make their robes white in the blood of the Lamb and thus through pain peace has come to them in the end.'

This hard-held belief that pain was the result of earlier sin and that its expiation by heroic endurance paved the road to eternal life was shared by both institutions at that time. Also common to both those and other denominations was a 'heightened concern about leakage and dechristianisation'. This was true in Ireland as well as England. There was one major difference between these two London hospices: the criteria for admission. In St Luke's only those of the 'respectable and deserving poor' were allowed in, whereas there was no such bar in the Hackney Hospice. In London there were Poor Law Institutions for 'the unworthy poor'. Nor did the Medical Superintendent of St Luke's have 'any qualms about dismissing patients whose moral character he felt was unsuitable'. The reasons for the refusal of the poor and destitute were many. One reason was the mindset of some Christian faiths at this time: unemployment and poverty were attributed to laziness and moral failure. The idea was not unknown in Dublin: the work ethos of Victorian times knew no frontiers.

Another major theme in religious outlook in early-twentieth-century times was deathbed 'conversions'. In Roman Catholic terms this usually meant reconciliation to the faith and practices of their baptism, occasionally it meant renunciation of a different form of Christianity—the 'leakage' referred to by Humphreys. The 'conversions' were two-way traffic. Despite anecdotal claims no national figures of such conversions or 'leakages' are available and publication of such statistics would be unpopular in these ecumenical times.

Of course the Roman Catholic emphasis on a holy and a happy death was not confined to hospices, whether in London or Dublin it was widespread among all who practised any faith. An organisation with this aim was that of the '*bona mors*' (a good death), which flourished in Victorian and twentieth-century times. Its numbers may have dwindled like those of many such organisations, but an Arch Confraternity of the Bona Mors is active to this day in at least one parish in Dublin's inner city. But attitudes to death have changed greatly: for some the idea of 'a good death' is very different as this contemporary quotation shows.

> Hospitals have become the place where the apparently terminal patient might almost miraculously be *rescued* from death. Doctors assumed control over the rituals of death: what was left of 'the good death' of the religious *ars moriendi* yielded to the priests in the white coats. . . . The modern doctor seemed to promise to overcome death. Rendered a mark of failure, death became a taboo, something to be deferred.[40]

Whether accepting this viewpoint or not it remains true that daily use of the words 'dying' 'death' or 'dead' is less common and no longer 'politically correct'.

At much the same time as that covered in the accounts of the two London hospices a Swedish doctor, Axel Munthe[41] described his experience of public hospitals in Paris, many then staffed by the Sisters of Charity of St Vincent de Paul, now called the Daughters of Charity. Munthe says he 'did not belong to their [Roman Catholic] creed' but describes them as 'invariably cheerful and happy . . . and also tolerant—those who believed and those who did not were all the same to them.'

In the Annals of Our Lady's Hospice there are a few mentions of deathbed conversions and repentances. In just one of these six-yearly reports total figures are given by an unnamed Sister—the reports in that era were anonymous as reticence then demanded. The time was the early 1920s. Having referred to 'stray sheep sent here to die' the Sister reports that 'over six years twenty-five converts from Protestantism were received into the Church and forty-three Roman Catholics were instructed and prepared for the Sacraments'.

This second group would be among the 'strayed sheep' and qualify for the term then popular of 'deathbed repentances'.

Such triumphalism would not be popular or politically correct today and must be taken in the context of those times. The 'connection with England' had been broken and the Irish Free State was in its infancy. Nationalism had won a victory, incomplete though it was. The Roman Catholic Church was reaching the apogee of its ascendancy in Ireland—at that time a militant Catholicism *was* politically correct.

But there is in the Annals of the Sisters a rather different story about changing religions, this time in the Edwardian days before the First World War.

In the Hospice there was a Church of Ireland lady of reduced circumstances. She was from Galway and was dying of cancer. This took a particularly vicious form in that the tumour was ulcerated.

At that time such cases of 'open cancer' could not be admitted to an 'open' i.e. multi-bedded ward; this was on medical grounds and for the benefit of the other patients: the stench from an ulcerated and infected tumour is not pleasant. The Galway woman had a wealthy Catholic friend and relative who arranged for a private room in the Hospice—there were a few such rooms. Before her admission the cancer patient had secured the adoption by her friend of one of her three children. The other two lodged in Kingstown (now Dún Laoghaire) in one of Mrs Smyly's Homes for orphaned or impoverished children, colloquially called 'The Bird's Nest'.

The patient's husband was 'a gentlemanly but characterless man devoted to his wife'. Because his wife wanted to become a Roman Catholic the husband took the boy from the 'Bird's Nest' and mother and son were baptised by the Roman rite.

The point about this story is that when the father went to take his son away from the Protestant institution to be baptised a Catholic 'the authorities there made no difficulty about surrendering their charge'. Ecumenism is not a new practice.

There is a sequel to this tale. The mother died a month later and 'her husband drifted out of sight but reappeared in a dying state' and was admitted to the Hospice. When the priest who had attended his wife approached him, the man said 'he wanted nothing about religion'. There were no further conversations with the priest but a week later he was sent for by the patient. Like his wife the man was baptised a Catholic and died a week later.

Forty years before the incident just related there was another example of interdenominational accord. In an Irish newspaper of April 1905 there is a brief report from the Dublin Diocesan Synod of the Church of Ireland at which Archbishop Peacocke is quoted as announcing

> . . . the foundation of a Home for the Dying where the Protestant poor may have the attention and soothing care that have made Our Lady's Hospice such a blessing to the Catholic poor of the city. Archbishop Peacocke

President Mary McAleese greets Cicely Saunders DBE at the International Palliative Care Conference June 2000.

On the occasion of their retirement, Dr P. O'Callaghan and Dr John Fleetwood flanking Sr Francis Rose.

The Palliative Care Unit opened in 1993.

The late Ms Kathy Kearns formerly ward sister with St Charles' Ward and Ms Hilary Brady, a leader in Home Care, now working in the Blackrock Hospice.

*Occupational therapy—the late Mrs
Aingeal Ó Catháin and her mentor
Gloria Smythe*

The front of the Hospice—the sun rooms were added in the 1970s.

Dr Maeve O'Reilly, Clinical Tutor, with a medical student

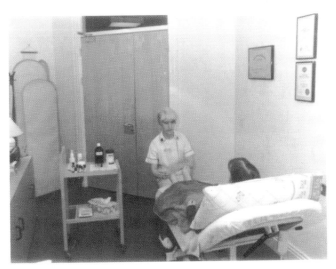

Aromatherapy—Sr Anne O'Halloran at work.

Our Lady's Hospice Board of Directors

Mr James Nugent (Chairman)

Sr Patrica Somers

Sr Francis Rose O'Flynn

Sr Jacinta Forde

Ms Teresa Harrington

Professor Helen Burke

Mr Seán Benton

Mr Joseph Davy

Dr Denis Keating

Dr Douglas Veale

Sr Helen McGilly, Dr Oliver FitzGerald, Dr Liam O'Siorain, Dr Denis Donohoe, Dr Michael Kearney, Michael Murphy, Sr Muriel Larkin with President Mary McAleese.

The High Altar in the main chapel, gift of Archbishop Murray

acknowledges that the good Sisters of Charity, who are the pioneers of this form of charity in these countries, never locked the door against a Protestant patient.

This generous tribute was prefaced by the remark that 'rivalry in well-doing is the most healthful of all rivalries'.

A hundred years later it is admitted by all that peoples' or nations' views about religion have changed greatly in the last century. There was a recent example of this in an Irish Sunday paper.[42] The heading was: 'Patients don't need spoonful of religion'—an ambiguous title. The author writes that 'in Ireland religious intrusion and harassment are sanctified and defined as 'caring spirituality'—this written because a friend of the reporter's of no denomination was bemused and offended by being offered Communion by a nurse each day. The article ends: 'There is no acceptance by the medical authorities that there are many people for whom the Catholic ethos in medicine is illiberal, dangerous and inhumanely authoritarian. Yet they have no choice but to submit to it.'

These are strong words. The quoted evidence for this opinion totals two cases which, as reported, certainly appear unacceptable. Anybody who spends one morning in any Dublin hospital and sees how patients are offered the chance to accept or refuse Communion is likely to disagree.

On this controversial subject, let me quote the words of the Director of a Church of England Palliative Care Hospice in Suffolk in England:

> I am in charge of people who are going to die within three months at the outside. I run you might say a crammer's course for death or eternity. It's not for me to choose which. I just help them to come to terms with their own choice.[43]

In Our Lady's Hospice all the staff would agree with this viewpoint. The fact that these words were spoken by a fictional character of Gavin Lyall's adds to their impact.

Another example from the literature of today is that of a German epidemiologist who writes:

> Because of the standardisation of life expectancy death looms over the
> final phase of life, i.e. over us in advanced age in many chronically incurable
> cases as never before. It reduces the quality of life and the quality of death.
> Moreover it is no longer eternity that awaits us but a passing away. We try to
> suppress both as far as possible. . . . If more and more people on earth had
> everything including a complete life span in good health then perhaps eter-
> nity would no longer be 'necessary'.[14]

One cannot help smiling at the academic caution of the qualify-
ing 'perhaps' and the quotation marks which weaken the emphasis
of the key word 'necessary'. The problem with this viewpoint is that
for many a belief in eternity remains unchanged, much as some
might like to abandon faith in the existence of God and of heaven
or hell. But whether holding these or other beliefs the dying in Our
Lady's Hospice will get 'the help to come to terms with their own
choice'.

The contrasting view to that mentioned above—'embracing'
rather than 'suppressing' death—was given at the Bás Solais Conference by Sister Una O'Neill. Commenting on the present ten-
dency to define and analyse everything in terms of market value
rather than the needs of people as people O'Neill made the point
that such thinking is part of

> . . . a death denying culture with life threatening consequences. The
> focus of this Conference is death and dying which presumes that we are
> people who have tried to face the reality, people who are trying to embrace
> their own death.

In embracing our death we are on the way of truth. In the South-
West of Ireland the Gaelic phrase which was used to tell of a person's death is: '*Tá sé are slí na fírinne*' 'He is on the road of truth'.
Once we have embraced the mortal character of our existence we
are 'on the road of truth'.

Up to now just eight reports from the chaplaincies of different faiths have been published. Unlike half a century earlier in the Annals there is no mention of 'reconciliation' or changes of faith. Nor is there any record of the successes or rebuffs experienced in the daily work of the chaplains. This of course holds true for all the kinds of care given in Our Lady's Hospice, whether the patient be the bed-bound senior citizen, the younger person disabled by joint disease or the patient of any age dying from cancer. To produce numbers or percentages, to apply accountancy to this vital form of patient care is fortunately impossible. The services provided by the Roman Catholic Pastoral Care team include :

Mass each day in the Hospice Chapel
Mass and the Sacrament of Reconciliation on request
Mass twice weekly in Palliative Care, where there is also a lunch-
    time prayer meeting most weeks
An evening visit to all the patients in Our Lady's Hospic
Arranging funeral services in the mortuary

Direct contact with patients and their families is the keystone of pastoral care. Establishing a two-way relationship with such people makes possible caring and fruitful contact before and after the time of death. Clearly the amount of time spent in each case varies greatly. Bereavement counselling may be needed. Of late there has been an annual bereavement Mass, held now in Mount Argus because of space demands, organised by Our Lady's Hospice and the Irish Hospice Foundation, and also an Ecumenical Service of Light in Our Lady's Hospice Education Centre.

The thinking, the ethos, behind pastoral care as practised today in Our Lady's Hospice is inseparable from that of palliative care. Both are all embracing, holistic and highly personal. Both are inter-disciplinary and dependant on team work. In recent years the term 'spirituality' has become popular: 'sensing the presence of God' is a definition of it that includes many faiths and that is not confined by the practices of organised religion. Twycross[44] has put this idea differently: 'the word 'spiritual' embraces the essence of what it means to be human', a definition which complements the one given above. It is clear that the terms ' spiritual' and 'religious' care are no longer synonymous, a distinction understandable today when multiple faiths and cultures flourish side by side in a shrinking world.

From definitions to their practical applications let me quote a chaplain in Our Lady's Hospice.[45]

> If the experience of Church or life is negative, spirituality [may] conjure up feelings of fear, guilt, regret and above all the absence of God. . . . When surrounded by a loving and caring team patients can and often do find God in themselves. The attitude [of the chaplain] is without judgement; we leave them space to be angry, to talk of their dark side safe in the knowledge that nothing they say or do will make us reject them.

Ethos has become a buzz word. The ethos of a hospital organisation or religious order is a very real and particular, but intangible and sometimes indefinable thing. The Greek word *ethos* means character and was defined by Aristotle as 'the prevalent tone of sentiment of a people or community; the genius of an institution or system; [perhaps] ideal excellence'.[46] Ethics is the study of the character and conduct of people—their morals. Ethos and ethics lead to action which if successful becomes mission effectiveness—this is the practical point where application of ethos becomes an everyday reality. And this is why in 1997 there started in Our Lady's Hospice an in-service education with this same title of 'Mission Effectiveness'. Two dozen members of staff from all departments attended workshops every week for five weeks. The cross section of disciplines made for good group discussions. An important result was a submission to the Executive Committee by each participant of the factors thought to be preventing the implementation of the core values of Our Lady's Hospice. These core values are listed as 'human dignity, compassion, justice, quality and advocacy . . . lived out in the Hospice by each of us no matter what our job description is'.

Death raises related issues such as spirituality, religion, physician-assisted suicide and euthanasia. These affect carers, relatives and friends as well as the patient. One of the core values of the Religious Sisters of Charity health services is human dignity, which is defined by them as 'respect for the sacredness of human life and the dignity of each person created in the image of God'. Knowing this, it is no surprise that euthanasia is not practised in Our Lady's Hospice; world-wide however it is a controversial issue.

A recent article[47] from the Netherlands is by two workers in the Departments of Ethics, Philosophy and History of Medicine in the University Medical Centre of Nijmegen. They analysed 12 palliative care journals over 13 years and found 75 publications on euthanasia up to 1999. Nearly half (46 per cent) of the articles took no stand on the issue of euthanasia, one sixth (16 per cent) favoured it, while one third (37 per cent) were against it. Plainly the issue is of current interest and likely to remain so. On the broader theme of 'ethics' there were 500 articles in the same journals. It would be surprising if there was agreement on the meaning of the word euthanasia; some subdivide it into 'voluntary' and 'imposed' euthanasia. Of more immediate and practical interest in the context of Irish hospices and hospitals is the related subject of the withdrawal of life support mechanisms, again controversial and much muddied by misunderstandings. The term 'right to die' includes the patient's right to autonomy; if there is unconsciousness the wishes of relatives become part of the puzzle; the medical judgement on the condition and outlook for the patient is a key piece in the same jigsaw; and clearly consultation with those concerned is an essential part of the puzzle solving. The dilemma and the decision depend on the ethos of each of the persons involved—these may differ and lead to difficulties. Such cases are rare but have occasionally happened in Our Lady's Hospice. But in an age of global communication and changing mores it would be surprising if these dilemmas did not become more common in Ireland. Already abortion is a controversial issue and at the other end of life, the way one dies has also become a matter for debate.

The Irish Association for Palliative Care has endorsed the right of the patient to refuse medical investigation and treatment.[48] It is a sad reflection on modern society that it was deemed necessary to reiterate this age old truth. Like the Medical Council of Ireland[49] and An Bord Altranais[50] the Association emphasises that it is the responsibility of the professionals to ensure that the patient dies with dignity, a way of death very different from the deliberate killing of a human being at the request of the patient—'voluntary euthanasia'. The frequency of such problems today is made manifest by the results of a European study of 20,000 deaths from all causes in 2001–2002: 'medical end-of-life decision making' took place in two-thirds of the patients whose death was not unexpected.[51] For those interested there is in the general news weekly *America* (5 April 2004) a succinct article by Gerald D. Coleman entitled 'Take and Eat: Morality and Medically Assisted Feeding' which gives the Roman Catholic outlook on this subject. In the same number there is an article headed 'Pope says Patients *must* Receive Nutrition, Hydration.' Rome has spoken.

A final point must be made. This is an era in which disciplines multiply in an endless fashion. Whatever the job, whether it be a commercial or a caring one, specialities grow in number and narrowness of focus. Diplomas and degrees distinguishing the subspecialities are part of this growth. How did Our Lady's Hospice survive and prosper for a century before labels like 'multidisciplinary teams' become common currency? Who made the system work? The answer is simple and quite clear: the Sisters of Charity—'the nuns' as they were called. Their numbers then were far more numerous and not all were registered nurses. Yet their life-long dedication to patient care in its most practical 'hands on' form was manifest to many, acknowledged by most and taken for granted by all.

15 A vision for the future

Sister Francis Rose O'Flynn

Our Lady's Hospice has always endeavoured to heed the signs of the times. In the twentieth century, it developed and up-graded its palliative care and rheumatology rehabilitation facilities. Now, the early twenty-first century poses two further challenges to its responsiveness to patient care. Firstly, the need to up-to-date patient care; secondly, the provision of a new building for the Education and Research Department is urgently required. By responding to these challenges it is hoped that the vision of the Hospice, born of a commitment to whole person care, will continue to develop and grow.

Continuing Care

One hundred and twenty-five years have passed since Our Lady's Hospice first opened its doors to seriously ill patients. A few years after the foundation Sister Mary John Gaynor realised the available space was inadequate to meet the demand for admission. With great courage she planned a building in 1886 to accommodate 110 patients. To meet yet another demand most of these beds were given over to continuing care of the frail elderly in the 1950s.

Recent developments include the conclusion of discussions between the Eastern Regional Health Authority (ERHA) and St James's Hospital Geriatric Division (MedEl) which has resulted in the opening of the Community Reablement Unit (CRU). This is an exciting initiative which seeks to delay the entrance of frail older people into continuing care by providing a period of rehabilitation for them. Such a new service is perhaps best described as 'intermediate care' in that patients are offered appropriate assistance and actively encouraged to return home with whatever community-based supports they may need to achieve this aim. Patients most suitable for this service, for example, include those with upper limb fractures, and/or a history of recurrent falls, which require investigation. The length of stay in a reablement programme would not normally exceed four to five weeks.

With this new service up and running Our Lady's Hospice realises the need for continuing care will still be a major factor in the twenty-first century. Demographic trends indicate that between 1996 and 2001 the over-65 age groups has increased by 100,771 making it 14.1 per cent of the total population. Allied to this, there is an increase in life expectancy Europe-wide. In short, people are living longer and this will have an impact on health systems and particularly on the need for continuing care. While there may be an amelioration of some of the conditions of old age due to medical advances, improvement in community services and reablement/rehabilitative facilities for older people, it is recognised that a proportion will still seek the services of Our Lady's Hospice for continuing care. For example, it is currently reckoned that 5 per cent of people over 65 years of age suffer from some form of dementia with the figures increasing with advancing age (20 per cent over 80, 25 per cent over 85). According to the Alzheimer Society of Ireland (2001), with people living longer, these figures may well double over the next 25 years.

With these factors in mind, and the age and condition of its present continuing care facility very much in evidence, Our Lady's Hospice embarked upon planning the first expansion and up-grading of its extended care beds since they were opened in 1879. A site for a 100-bed unit, including day care and therapy facilities, was provided within the existing grounds. The expectation was that this very necessary development would be funded under the National Development Plan with the support of the South Western Area Health Board (SWAHB) and the Eastern Regional Health Authority (ERHA). With that in mind, planning approval was obtained in 2002 and hopes were high. However, progress to tender was rendered impossible because of a countrywide lack of finance of major capital developments. This was a major setback but the Hospice is committed to the highest standards of continuing care for older people who require its services. Thus, it continues to advocate for their needs with the ERHA and the Department of Health and Children. With a long tradition of faith and courage behind it, Our Lady's Hospice is determined to provide the best possible care for the vulnerable sectors of society who seek its services. Our Lady's Hospice is prepared to engage with the challenges of the times and respond innovatively to them.

In the late nineteenth century, the Sisters of Charity perceived an urgent need and moved forward with few resources and much faith to meet it. This ethos permeates the Hospice mission and is shared by its staff who are prepared to give ear to the signs of the times and respond innovatively to them. This is honed by active multidisciplinary discussion and debate within the Hospice and a commitment to education, research and development. Aspirations and advocacy must be backed by well-documented evidence. It is with this in mind that the twenty-first century sees huge developments and potential in Our Lady's Hospice Education and Research Department—the second of its two great challenges.

Education, research and training at Our Lady's Hospice: the way ahead

Our Lady's Hospice puts forward a vision of health care which is much needed in today's world: a vision which 'strives through a team approach and in an atmosphere of loving care to promote wholeness of body, mind and spirit' (mission statement). Education, research and training provide the bedrock of a quality service to patients and their families. Since 1987 Our Lady's Hospice has offered education programmes to healthcare professionals both inside and outside the Hospice. The care of patients has changed beyond recognition in recent years with the development of new treatments and multifaceted modes of intervention. Professional care and practice must be soundly evidence-based on up-to-date national and international research. In the case of Our Lady's Hospice, this is a huge task as it must encompass the three specialisms of palliative care, rheumatology and care of the older person.

In the past and currently, members of the education team are involved in research projects at Master and PhD levels related to the areas of rheumatology, gerontology and palliative care. They also contribute to national and international journals and conferences. Thus, for example, 2003 has seen presentations in Dublin, Manchester, Orlando, USA and Barcelona. It is the aspiration of the education team to keep up and indeed, increase this level of involvement with the research community.

In regard to medical education at Our Lady's Hospice, and especially palliative medicine, the future is full of potential. The Education and Research Department is currently linked with the medical faculties of both University College Dublin and Trinity College Dublin. A medical tutor and a physiotherapy tutor are involved in the education of undergraduate medical students, while post-graduate specialist registrar programmes are available. In palliative medicine there is also a general practitioner training rotation. The vision for Our Lady's Hospice in the twenty-first century is to further develop and strengthen these third-level links by the setting up of a joint Chair in Palliative Medicine with University College Dublin and Trinity College Dublin.

Nurse education continues to meet the challenges presented to it. With the advent of the Higher Diploma in Nursing Studies (palliative nursing) eleven years ago, Our Lady's Hospice became the leading centre for palliative nursing in Ireland. However, this was only a beginning. Our Lady's Hospice education team has been instrumental in driving forward further developments in post-graduate nursing education: namely the Higher Diplomas in Nursing Studies (rheumatology rehabilitation and gerontological nursing) which commenced in partnership with University College Dublin in 2001. Thus, currently Our Lady's Hospice is the education and clinical training/placement site for three post-graduate nursing programmes.

Because of its established reputation in skilled nursing care of the older person, Our Lady's Hospice was approached by both University College Dublin and Trinity College Dublin to facilitate clinical placements for their undergraduate (BSc Nursing) students from 2002 onwards. Our Lady's Hospice education team has taken up this challenge and are currently in the process of negotiating additional clinical placements in the Hospice's rheumatology rehabilitation services. Thus, nurse education in the Hospice encompasses both undergraduate and post-graduate development.

In regard to the paramedical disciplines, Our Lady's Hospice is an accredited fieldwork placement site for undergraduate students of occupational therapy and physiotherapy, as it is for professional social work training. In the case of the latter, students come not only from the two aforementioned Dublin universities but also from University College Cork.

Penultimately, Our Lady's Hospice Education Department offers training to care assistants and its team facilitate a Level 2 FETAC (Further Education and Training Awards Council) National Certificate Course in Care Skills for Care Assistants which consists of eight modules. This is the new national standard of training for care assistants as approved by the Republic of Ireland's Department of Health and Children. The vision and aim for the future is that it would provide professional healthcare staff and ultimately patients with skilled and knowledgeable support in service provision.

Finally, the education team hopes to continue to provide other courses and study days related to the needs of the multifaceted healthcare service provided by the Hospice and other organisations which seek its assistance and skills.

Thus, the Education and Research Department of Our Lady's Hospice seeks to meet the challenges of the twenty-first century with intellectual vigour and commitment to a vision of patient care which 'strives though a team approach and in an atmosphere of loving care to promote wholeness of body, mind and spirit' (mission statement).

Conclusion

In conclusion, Our Lady's Hospice has always endeavoured to heed the signs of the times. In the twentieth century it developed and upgraded its palliative care and rheumatology rehabilitation facilities. Indeed the development of a satellite unit for specialist palliative care in Blackrock, Co. Dublin, through the generosity of the Louis and Zelie Martin Foundation, is testimonial to our continued commitment and responsiveness to the needs of the underserviced. Now, the early twenty-first century poses two further challenges to its responsiveness to patient care. Firstly, the need to upgrade and expand the current facilities for the continuing care of older people presents itself. Secondly, because education and research form the bedrock of up-to-date patient care, the provision of a new building for the Education and Research Department is urgently required. By responding to these challenges, it is hoped that the vision of the Hospice, born of a commitment to whole person care, will continue to develop and grow. 'The glory of God is Man fully alive' (t. Irenaeus of Lyon). Our Lady's Hospice would wish for no less for those who seek its services at whatever stage of life's journey they find themselves on.

Sr Francis Rose O'Flynn
Board of Directors, Our Lady's Hospice, and former Chairperson
Former Superior General, Religious Sisters of Charity

Appendix 1 Chronology

1815	*Religious Sisters of Charity (RSC) founded by Mary Aikenhead in Dublin*
1843	Jeanne Garnier starts a Hospice for the dying in Lyons, France
1845	*Greenmount House (later Our Lady's Mount), Harold's Cross purchased by the Religious Sisters of Charity*
1845	Ireland's Great Famine starts
1858	*Mary Aikenhead, Foundress of the RSC dies*
1870	St Patrick's (Marymount) Hospital opened in Cork by RSC
1879	*Our Lady's Hospice for the Dying, Harold's Cross, opens*
1879	Land League founded by Michael Davitt in Mayo, Ireland
1886	*New building for 90 patients begins in Harold's Cross*
1890	Sacred Heart Hospice (RSC) opens in Sydney, Australia
1905	St Joseph's Hospice opened by RSC in Hackney, London
1906	Arthur Griffith founds Sinn Féin (We ourselves) in Dublin
1910	*Our Lady's Hospice acquires 13 acres*
1914	Home Rule Bill for Ireland passed by UK Parliament
1914–18	First World War
1916	Rebellion in Dublin
1918	Sinn Féin successful in General Election
1919–21	War of Independence in Ireland
1920	December: Government of Ireland Act—Partition
1921	June: Stormont Parliament for Northern Ireland opened
1921	July: Truce in Anglo-Irish War
1921	December: Anglo-Irish Treaty
1922	December: Treaty enacted. Handover of Dublin Castle by UK
1922–23	Civil War in Ireland
1930	*Rathmines—and Hospice—incorporated into Dublin City*
1937	Irish Free State (Saorstát Eireann) becomes Éire under new constitution

1939–45	Second World War; food and fuel rationing in neutral Éire
1949	Republic of Ireland declared
1961	*St Joseph's Rheumatology Unit opens in Our Lady's Hospice*
1964	*Chemotherapy unit opens in OLH; 'Dying' dropped from title of Our Lady's Hospice (OLH)*
1967	St Christopher's Hospice opens in London
1972	Violence in Northern Ireland begins
1977	*Palliative Care starts in OLH*
1985	*Home Care Service starts*
1986	*Bereavement Support starts*
1987	Marian (Educational) Unit opened
1989	St Francis Hospice commences Palliative Care service
1989	Fall of Berlin Wall
1991	*The farm closes*
1993	*New building for Palliative Care*
1993	Good Friday agreement in Northern Ireland
1994	*New Mortuary*
1997	Hydrotherapy pool opened
2000	*First International Palliative Care Conference (Bás Solais) held in Ireland organised by OLH in conjunction with the Irish Cancer Society*
2000	*New restaurant opened*
2003	*A second RSC Hospice opens in Blackrock, Co. Dublin*
2004	*New building for Extended Care commences*

Appendix 2 Places of peace and worship

Sister Helen Cunningham and T. M. Healy

What follows is a shortened version, with some additions, of Sister Joseph Helen Cunningham's holograph account of the main Chapel in Our Lady's Hospice and how it has changed and developed since its opening in May of 1859. This was twenty years before the Hospice started, when the community consisted of Sisters and novices and there were no patients. When the Chapel was refurbished in 2001 a display case was put up in the porch; in the case are details about altars and statues as seen in the photograph on page 89. This case is seen in the accompanying photograph and in it are described the origins of altars, statues and windows.

The reredos and altar below it are the work of the five Farrell brothers of Dublin. The figures above the altar are: in the centre Christ kneeling at Peter's feet, flanked by four saints—two Jesuit priests and two 'fathers' of families. From left to right they are Stanislaus Kostka, Joseph Calasanctius, Ignatius Loyola and Joseph of Nazareth. All four of these men worked with the young; when it is remembered that Harold's Cross had been the Novitiate of the order the choice is understandable. The novices gone, equally young patients sometimes took their place for short spells before their death.

Less than two years before the Chapel was finished Mary Aikenhead died. Her congregation was free to commemorate her not just by the written word but in stained glass windows in the Chapel. These memorial windows both show Aikenhead and some of the Sisters. On the left there is a Latin inscription from the '*Te Deum*', that hymn of praise and thanksgiving. On the right are representations of the Sisters at work, teaching children and caring for the dying.

It must be very rare for the foundress of a new religious order to be commemorated within a couple of years of her death in such a permanent and striking fashion as stained glass. The windows were the gift of two Dublin firms: the stationers Browne & Nolan and the builders Messrs Beardwood—these two firms had worked for Mary Aikenhead in earlier times. The artist of the stained glass is unknown; he or she may have worked in the Earley Studios in Dublin. Both windows appear to be from the same hand.

Over the years there were additional alterations. The main points of the list are:

1907 Cloister of the Sacred Heart built. This was to balance that on the other or north side, called the Cloister of Our Lady. The entrance to the north transept retains the granite carving identifying it as a previous external entrance. With the recent building of the Aikenhead Heritage Centre close by, this 'cloister' is now a short cul-de-sac used to store a reserve of seats.

1930 The original stalls or side facing seats were replaced by kneelers and chairs, with a few benches at the back.

1937 To celebrate the golden jubilee of five Sisters the Community presented a mosaic floor for the sanctuary; it includes the congregational crest: the logo of the Sisters of Charity. The wrought iron Communion rails, one of the earliest examples of such work in Ireland, were moved to the organ loft.

1945 New Stations of the Cross in cream coloured plaster: again these came from the Earley Studios. The statue of the Sacred Heart was moved outside the Chapel door and replaced on the side altar by St Joseph.

1962 Dampness under the tesselated floor was a long-running problem. Each cube (tessera) of this floor had been bought for one old penny, thousands of which had been donated by the poor of Dublin at the time the Chapel was built. Not to uproot this example of nineteenth-century charity the multi-coloured floor was covered by matting and with parquet on top.

1970 Following the Second Vatican Council the altar was changed to face the congregation.

1979 A TV camera was installed for the closed circuit televising of the Mass to the wards for those bed-bound, long-stay patients unable to make the wheel-chair journey to the Chapel.

2001 The third millennium saw the introduction of furniture of a more modern type: single seats without kneelers. The floor is now carpeted. A bell no longer tolls for Mass but the organ and its loft survive. Adequate space for the wheelchair patients remains in the place of honour at the top; their usual number is about 25, fluctuating if Mass is said in one of the wards.

Despite these changes Anna Gaynor would have no difficulty in recognising the Chapel built in Aikenhead's memory. The degree of modern comfort might surprise her, but so too would many other of the changed practices of her faith. Yet the essentials remain the same. What none of the founding Sisters would recognise is the oratory in the Palliative Care Unit. The oratory is part of the E-shaped red brick building designed by John L. Griffith & Partners, and opened by President Mary Robinson in 1993. The oratory is dominated by the large stained glass crucifixion, a striking work by the school of Harry Clarke. It stands behind the altar and is lit from behind and was a gift from the Mill Hill Fathers following the closure of their house in Freshford, Co. Kilkenny. A life size depiction of a dying man is appropriate in a terminal care unit, and the dying Christ has the support of his mother and her adopted son, John.

The families of the dying or deceased find this chapel a place of solace. One visiting mother got her five-year-old son to walk from one side to the other of the oratory so that he could observe for himself 'the way Christ's eyes follow you'. Dressing-gowned patients use the oratory freely and some are wheeled there by their friends. At Mass times others arrive in wheelchairs and are joined by their families and members of staff.

On the first floor of the Rheumatology Rehabilitation Unit, beside the Sacred Heart Ward, there is a third place of Roman Catholic worship—whether called chapel or oratory depends on the vocation of the speaker. It is used by patients and staff, present or retired. Surrounded by the rooms of staff headquarters is a small place of prayer: God and Mammon in close proximity. This islet of peace is off the first floor corridor of the main building, unobtrusive and silent.

In the grounds statues of Our Lady have been mentioned—all have survived the test of time and the expansion of building. What has gone is the Calvary which once stood outside the mortuary; this happened when the mortuary was extended in 1984. Newly sited is another statue, much cherished by the Sisters as a favourite of their foundress Mary Aikenhead. Chairbound though she was, she could see it from her room, placed as the statue then was on top of the school. When the school closed the statue was moved to the Sisters' school in Henrietta Street opposite the King's Inns. When the Big House became the Aikenhead Heritage Centre the statue returned to its Harold's Cross home and now stands below the window of Aikenhead's old room. Fittingly this much travelled statue is of Our Lady. Carved from Portland stone it is a little larger than life size and rests on the ground giving an impression of friendly approachability; this was made evident when some workmen from outside did not hesitate to hang their jackets on her outstretched hand.

Appendix 3 Rectresses/Superiors, Our Lady's Hospice

1879–97	Mary John (Anna) Gaynor
1897–1908	Agnes Gertrude Chamberlain
1908–19	James Francis Ryan
1919–24	Bernard Mary Carew
1924–30	Petronella Cannon
1930–35	Agnes Eucharia O'Brien
1935–41	Lelia Butler
1941–44	Malachy Costello
1944–56	Polycarp Cummins
1962–68	Francis Joan O'Rourke
1968–74	Teresa Avila Osborne
1974–83	Joseph Ignatius Phelan
1983–90	Francis Rose O'Flynn
1990–96	Eilis Mulhern
1997–99	Muriel Larkin
2000–03	Jacinta Forde
2003–	Xavier Walshe

Matron*
1993–	Helena Marie McGilly

*Until 1992 the Superior was also the Matron.

Appendix 4 Physicians to Our Lady's Hospice

(Including Long Stay/Extended Care from 1978)

1879–95	Dudley White
1891–1915	Michael Francis Cox
1896–1915	* Garret Waters Joyce
1903–08	* Michael Strahan
1908–15	* Robert Percy McDonnell
1912–20	Joseph Daniel
1940–55	* Michael J. Mullen
1940–50	* Patrick T. O'Farrell
1953–54	Fergus Shiel
1950–53	* Risteárd Mulcahy
1962–90	* Patrick A. O'Callaghan
1962–90	John F. Fleetwood
1990–	Denis Donohoe

* *approximate dates*

Chemotherapy

1970–74	James J. Fennelly

Rheumatology Rehabilitation (St Joseph's Unit)

1962–89	Jack Molony
1978–	Barry Bresnihan
1990–	Oliver FitzGerald
2001–	Douglas Veale

Palliative Care

1978–89	Jack McCarthy
1989–96	Michael Kearney
1995–	Liam O'Siorain
2001–	Maeve O'Reilly
2001–	Eoin Tiernan

Home Care

1985–95	Veronie Hanley
1995–	Patricia Tuomey

Appendix 5 Heads of Departments in 2004

Michael Murphy	Chief Executive Officer
Dr Liam O'Siorain	Medical Director, Palliative Care Unit
Dr Maeve O'Reilly	Consultant in Palliative Medicine
Dr Peter Lawlor	Consultant in Palliative Medicine
Dr Eoin Tiernan	Consultant in Palliative Medicine
Dr Denis Donohoe	Medical Director, Extended Care & Community Reablement Units
Dr Miriam Casey	Consultant Geriatrician
Dr Douglas Veale	Medical Director, Rheumatology Rehabilitation Unit
Prof. Barry Bresnihan	Consultant Rheumatologist
Prof. Oliver FitzGerald	Consultant Rheumatologist
Sister Helena McGilly	Director of Nursing
Frances Murphy	Assistant Director of Nursing, Extended Care & Rheumatology Rehabilitation
Jacqueline Holmes	Assistant Director of Nursing, Palliative Care
Marianne McGiffin	Nurse Tutor
Mary Byrne	Clinical Nurse Manager, St Camillus Ward
Mary T. Carroll	Clinical Nurse Manager, St Camillus Ward
Aurie O'Sullivan	Clinical Nurse Manager, St Paul's Ward
Norah O'Connor	Clinical Nurse Manager, St Charles Ward

Eithne O'Rourke	Clinical Nurse Manager, St Mary's and St Joseph's Ward
Karen McElwaine	Clinical Nurse Manager, Community Reablement Unit
Chris Dalton	Clinical Nurse Manager, St Patrick's Ward
Michelle Lynch	Clinical Nurse Manager, Sacred Heart Ward
Eileen Shinners	Clinical Nurse Manager, St Teresa's Ward
Siobhan Sheehan	Clinical Nurse Manager, St Catherine's Ward
Margaret Byrne	Clinical Nurse Manager, St Gabriel's Ward
Breda Flynn	Human Resources Manager/Deputy Chief Executive Officer
Denis Maguire	Financial Controller
Monica Gilligan	Office Manager
Deirdre Rowe	Occupational Therapy Manager
Eithne Walsh	Physiotherapy Manager
Ann Keating	Principal Social Worker
Sister Anne O'Halloran	Complementary & Creative Arts Therapies Co-Ordinator
Fr Casimir Haran	Chaplain
Sister Fiona Corway	Chaplain
Sister Laboure Sinnott	Mortuary Pastoral Care Co-Ordinator
Roisin Adams	Chief Pharmacist
Karen Creagh	Senior Radiographer
Helen Groves	Admissions Officer
Vicki Ann Ryan	Fundraising Co-Ordinator
Elaine Toal	Risk Manager
Seamus O'Connor	Fire Prevention Officer
Dolores Kenny	Household Supervisor
Nancy Byrne	Catering Manager
Carmel Glynn	Restaurant Manager

James Cooke	Purchasing & Materials Manager
Aodhan McNulty	IT Support Officer
Walter Walsh	Volunteer Co-Ordinator
Carolyn Roe	Volunteer Co-Ordinator
Breda Doran	Reception/Switchboard Supervisor
Linda Doyle	Reception/Switchboard Supervisor
Tommy Beatty	Building Services Manager
Eileen Nolan	Gardening/Grounds Manager
Dr. Sheelagh O'Brien	Occupational Health Doctor

Notes & References

Notes

1 Australia

In Sydney, Australia the RSC Sacred Heart Hospice for the Dying was opened in 1890. 'Forty beds are constantly occupied, though deaths occur so frequently that the occupants are often changed [*sic*]. Supported entirely by the charity of the people the Hospice is known as the "pearl of charities".'

The Australian province was recognised by Urban VIII in 1842 but due to the dilatoriness of the Vicar General, Dr Gregory, the province was not activated until four years later. It became independent from Harold's Cross and is today a separate province.

All above comes courtesy of John and Maev O'Meara who also provided the reference: Margaret Donovan's book on Aikenhead (Melbourne 1979).

2 Lord Edward FitzGerald

Before his arrest in Dublin by Major Sirr in 1798 FitzGerald sought brief refuge in Greenmount, the house that was to become Marymount and the Hospice. In compliment to his hosts, the Webbs, he was disguised as a Quaker.

3 David Aikenhead

This Scotsman, based in Cork, was father to Mary, foundress of the RSC. In eighteenth- and nineteenth-century times apothecaries were the general practitioners or family doctors of the day. Their qualification came from the Apothecaries' ['Pots'] Hall in Dublin. If they were also Licentiates of the Royal College of Physicians in Dublin, Edinburgh or, less likely, London, they were entitled to be called 'Doctor'. Not so surgeons or dentists.

4 Long service records

Unlike today's shuttling by staff of all kinds, for most of Our Lady's Hospice's existence lengthy service in that place was the norm for RSC Sisters. These examples are typical: three nuns who joined the Hospice in the first decade of its existence gave from 42 to 45 years of their lives to Harold's Cross. All died in the Hospice. One of these, Sister Matthew Nugent died as recently as December

1979 aged about 90.

Although, as noted earlier, the number of Sisters has shrunk, in the ten years before 1976 their total complement ranged between 16 and 21 and many of these would have approached Sister Nugent's record of service.

5 The mission statement of the Hospice
Since 1998 there is a plaque to the left of the main door of the 1889 building. The mission statement of Our Lady's Hospice reads: 'Founded in 1879 by the Sisters of Charity Our Lady's Hospice strives through a team approach in an atmosphere of loving care to promote wholeness of body, mind and spirit'.

References

1 *Shorter Oxford English Dictionary*, Vol. I, p 925, Oxford 1959.
2 Kerr, B., *Am. J. of Hospice and Palliative Care*, pp 13–20, May–June 1993.
3 Burke, Helen, *The Royal Hospital Donnybrook*, p 5, Dublin, 1993.
4 Humphreys, C. J., *Tuberculosis, Poverty and the First Hospices in Ireland*, Bás Solais, Dublin 2000.
5 O'Brien, J. V., *'Dear, Dirty Dublin'*, p 102, London 1982.
6 O'Brien, J. V., *op. cit.*, p 130.
7 Pim, F. W. *Preventable Diseases: Why Are They Not Prevented?* p 14, Dublin 1892.
8 Somerville Large, P., *Dublin—The First Thousand Years*, p 249, Belfast 1988.
9 Blake, D. S., *Mary Aikenhead: Servant of the Poor*, Dublin 2001.
10 Atkinson, S., *Mary Aikenhead—Her Life, Her Work and Her Friends*, Dublin 1886.
11 Joyce, W. St John, *The Neighbourhood of Dublin*, pp 191–2, Dublin 1912.
12 Powell, M. Bernard (Ed.), *A City Set on a Hill: Our Lady's Hospice (OLH) 1845–1945*, p 20, Dublin 1945.
13 Butler, Katherine, *We Help them Home*, p 17, Dublin 1979.
14 Granshaw, L. in Wear, A. (Ed.), *Medicine in Society*, p 199, Cambridge 1992.
15 Butler, *op. cit.*, p 14.
16 Fleetwood, J., letter to the author, 8 Nov. 2001.
17 O'Farrell, P. T., in Powell *op. cit*, pp 35, 46.
18 Molony, J., letter to the author, 3 Nov. 2001.
19 Bresnihan, B., conversation with the author, 21 Aug. 2003.
20 Mulcahy, R., *Richard Mulcahy 1886–1971. A Family Memoir*, Dublin 1999.
21 Donohoe, D., interview given to the author.
22 Saunders, C., Kastenbraum, R. (Eds.), *Hospice Care on the International Scene*, pp 4–5, New York 1997.
23 McCarthy, J. in Butler, K. *op. cit.*, p 39.
24 *Annual Report*, OLH 1986, pp 7, 8.
25 *Annual Report*, OLH 1987, p 15.
26 Phelan, Ignatius, interview given to the author, 18 Nov. 2002.

27 McDonnell, M., in *Our Lady's Hospice Review 1990–1993* (no pagination).
28 Neuberger, Max, quoted in Doolin, W. *Wayfarers in Medicine*, Dublin 1949, p 15.
29 *Annual Report*, OLH 1986, p 18.
30 *Annual Report*, OLH 2000, p 5.
31 *Annual Report*, OLH 1987 p 16.
32 Pierce, Patricia, personal communication, July 2002.
33 Walsh, E. in *Annual Report*, OLH 2000, pp 30–31.
34 *Annual Report*, OLH 1999, p 27.
35 Dagg, V., in *Our Lady's Hospice Review 1994–1997*, pp 18–19.
36 Curtis, J., *Harold's Cross*, pp 148–9, Dublin 2001.
37 O'Shea, J., interview given to the author, 13 May 2002.
38 Sheridan, F., report from Arborist Associates Ltd., Mar. 2001, courtesy of Eileen Nolan.
39 Humphreys, C. J., 'Soul Curers: Spiritual and Physical Care in the Early Hospices', Bás Solais 2000.
40 Porter, R., *The Greatest Benefit to Mankind*, pp 692–3, London 1997.
41 Munthe, A., *The Story of San Michele*, p 41 of 1975 reprint, Suffolk 1929.
42 O'Kelly, E., *Sunday Independent*, 2 Sept. 2001, p 10.
43 Lyall, G., *The Crocus List*, London 1985, p 287.
14 Imhoff, A., in Wear, A. (Ed.), *op. cit.*, p 375.
44 Twycross, R. G., *Mud and Stars—The Impact of Hospice Experience on the Church's Ministry of Healing*, London 1991.
45 Corway, F., 'The Divine Healer in Palliative Care', MA thesis for Dublin City University, 2002.
46 *Shorter Oxford English Dictionary*, Vol. I, p 637.
47 Hermsen, M.A., ten Have Hamj, 'Euthanasia in Palliative Care Journals', *Journal of Pain and Symptom Management*, 23, 517–526, 2002.
48 O'Brien, T., McQuillan, R., Smullen H., *Voluntary Euthanasia*, Dublin 2000.
49 The Medical Council of Ireland, *A Guide to Ethical Conduct and Behaviour and Fitness to Practice*, Dublin 1989.
50 An Bord Altranais, *The Code of Professional Conduct for each Nurse and Midwife*, Dublin 1989.
51 Heide, vander, Agnes, *et al*, 'End of life decision-making in six European countries: Descriptive study' *The Lancet 2003* Vol. 361 pp 245–353.

Index